JUNKET TO JAPAN

Haro, Japan

TO JUNKET TO JAPAN

by Clarissa Lorenz

with photographs from
Peter Bell's excursion

Little, Brown and Company
Boston
Toronto

Second Printing

The photographs opposite pages 38 and 39 and the bottom photograph opposite page 175 were taken and are copyright by George Holton.

Published simultaneously in Canada
by Little, Brown & Company (Canada) Limited

PRINTED IN THE UNITED STATES OF AMERICA

Dedicated to Peter Dexter Bell, that intrepid ambassador of good will, and to the American Field Service, which made it all possible.

"Walk together,
  Talk together
O ye peoples of the earth:
  then and only then
shall ye have peace"

Motto of the American Field Service

This book, partly fictionalized, is based on Peter Bell's adventures in Japan.

CONTENTS

ILLUSTRATIONS

FOREWORD

This is the story of Peter Dexter Bell, who spent a summer with a Buddhist family in Tokyo. He and eight other American high school juniors were the first group ever to set foot in Japan on an American Field Service scholarship. They had been chosen as good-will ambassadors from among twenty-five hundred candidates in seven hundred schools.

This student-exchange project, designed to encourage better international understanding among the world's youth, is an outgrowth of the American Field Service, which goes back to World War I, when Americans supplied and drove ambulances in France. After World War II, Mr. Stephen Galatti, Director-General of the American Field Service, launched teen-age scholarships in the cause of international friendship. (Post-college grants had been in effect from 1919 to 1942, gradually diminishing until discontinued in 1951.)

In 1947 about fifty French and other foreign students

were enrolled in American schools and colleges for a ten-month period. As a reciprocal gesture, nine American teen-agers were invited to spend the following summer abroad, with families found by the French returnees. Since then both the short and long projects have mushroomed and with spectacular success.

The summer program is entirely self-sustaining, each American student being backed by five hundred and twen-ty-five dollars from either his family, community or both. It is run by A.F.S. students who have spent a year in the United States. These returnees locate host families in their own country and raise funds for sight-seeing tours. Expenses in Japan for Peter's group were met by the *Asahi Evening News* and the Tokyo Rotary Club.

The winter school program is restricted to foreign stu-dents, their families or communities paying a basic fee of six hundred and fifty dollars. American A.F.S. volunteers raise money, locate foster families here and interest schools in waiving tuition fees. Peter's mother is one of these vol-unteers. Any high school enrolling a foreign AFSer may nominate candidates for the program. They are selected on a competitive basis, a student-faculty committee screening applicants. They must be of high caliber and top academic standing, in good health, very adaptable and emotionally stable.

Peter measured up to all these requirements. An A-1 student, thoughtful and conservative, he was rather mature for his sixteen years, although fitting into any age group. History, sociology and political science were his major interests at Gloucester High, in Massachusetts. He was co-editor of the school weekly and president of the local chapter of the National Honor Society.

Like his parents, Mr. and Mrs. Harold Bell, Peter is tall, slim and blue-eyed, the eldest of six Bells — four boys and two girls. He was born and raised in Gloucester, where he lives in a spacious white clapboard house overlooking the Bass Rocks golf course. His hobbies include stamp collecting and photography. His father, treasurer of the Cape Ann Manufacturing Company, helped to finance his passage to Japan, while his Japanese family fed and housed him.

Now at Yale, Peter regards his experience in Japan as particularly valuable, since he hopes to enter the diplomatic service. His trip has made him an incurable Japophile. The illustrated talks he has given on Japan at various schools and clubs have broken down countless prejudices. "I no longer think of the Japanese as another race or culture," he said. "They're as close to me as my own brothers and sisters."

There's an old Irish proverb: "It's easy to see when you look with your heart." Peter saw Japan with his heart — the kind of vision that leads to international understanding and friendship.

JUNKET TO JAPAN

Peter Bell

Kozo

I
DESTINATION: JAPAN

I got the shock of my young life one balmy day in May when I came home from Gloucester High and my mother rushed to meet me, all excited.

"Sit down, Peter. I have news for you."

"What's up?" I dropped my books on the hall table, wondering if some relative had died and left me a fortune.

"Now keep calm," said she, in a twitter herself. "You're going to Japan."

"What?" I fell into a chair, staring. "But, Mother, the State Department doesn't allow exchange students in the Orient."

"Well, they do now. Here's the letter." She handed it to me with a sigh. "Oh dear, I don't know whether to weep or jump for joy at this change in your plans! Still Japan is so very different from Europe, and it will be an entirely new experience for you — a golden opportunity, too."

The letter from the American Field Service informed me

that I'd be staying with the Okajimas, a Buddhist family near Tokyo. "I don't know what to say. I'm all at sea."

"In another month you *will* be." She laughed. "Only on the Pacific instead of the Atlantic."

Had anyone told me that I'd be spending the summer in the Orient I would have said he must have a few buttons missing. In March, when the principal of Gloucester High broke the good news that I had won that AFS grant, I naturally assumed I'd be going to Europe, and the *Gloucester Times* had printed the story. People kept stopping me in the street and asking why I didn't see my own country first. My answer was that I *had* been to Colorado, Maine and Virginia.

What a shock they would get now! Like any other small town, Gloucester had its share of prejudices. We Yankees like our own ways of doing things and our own people. Summer visitors are okay, but different – outsiders, you know. My parents raised all six of us without any racial prejudices, but then I had never known any Japanese. My companions were mostly fishermen's children. Anything more alien than Orientals I couldn't imagine, and what I knew about Japan could have been put in a thimble – four main islands, Honshu, Kyushu, Hokkaido, Shikoku, besides some three thousand smaller ones. I would have to re-orient myself (no pun intended), readjust my whole line of thinking, and learn the language – all in four weeks' time.

Luckily one of my father's employees was a Japanese woman, and Kazue Oishi (*oishi* means delicious) offered to coach me. She was naturally thrilled about my proposed

4

trip. She had come from Kyushu, which I later learned was
Mrs. Okajima's birthplace, and had married an American
serviceman. It was his old army dictionary that I was to
carry to Japan. I laughed at the moth-eaten phrases in it —
"Put up your hands . . . Surrender . . . Clean out the la-
trines!"

A visitor to Japan, I had read somewhere, needs to know
only one word — *dozo* (please). In the next month I acquired a smattering of Japanese — *gomen nasai* (pardon
me), *arigato* (thank you), *ano-ne* (it's like this). What a
weird language — no *l*'s, *v*'s, *th* sounds, articles or plurals!
The Japanese use *san* in place of Mister, Mrs. or Miss. I'd
be called Peter-san, or, more formally, Bell Peter, since the
family name comes first.

Kazue briefed me about Nipponese customs — taking off
your shoes at the door, sitting on your haunches, eating with
chopsticks (*hashi*), and sleeping on a mattress or *futon*. "In
Japan," said she in her soft, flutelike voice, "you bow instead of shaking hands. The number and depth of bows depends on one's social status. Everything in Japan has meaning, and many ordinary things are held sacred. Tearing off
flowers, for instance, would be an insult. Watch what others do and you won't go wrong."

I promised to keep my eyes and ears open. A pity I
wouldn't get there in time for the cherry-blossom festival!
But four sights I was determined not to miss — geisha girls,
Kyoto, the Kabuki Theater and Fujiyama. Kozo, the Okajima's sixteen-year-old son, had written me a letter describ-
ing the sacred mountain (I suspect Kozo had a little help
from a guidebook):

5

"Mt. Fuji is the highest and most beautiful mountain in Japan, rising from the plains in a long, gentle, conical shape to a height of 12,467 feet. Throughout the year its peak is covered with snow. The season for scaling the mountain is generally limited to the months of July and August. However, the base districts with its five lakes and extensive forests constitute a year-around resort . . ."

Japan had already begun to fascinate me. I couldn't wait to see it. "You'll never be lonely or unhappy in the Land of the Rising Sun," one of our Cape Ann artisans told me. "I've been in twenty-four countries, but I felt most at home in Japan. The people are wonderfully kind and friendly."

Some Gloucester folks were horrified at my going. They still thought of Japan as the Yellow Peril and the Japanese as those treacherous Nips. One woman remarked to Mother, "Well, I'm glad it's not *my* boy who's going!" Unfortunately, the ship that was to take me there had just brought America an unwelcome cargo — Asian flu.

What with the last-minute switch in plans, I scurried around like a grasshopper getting my visa changed, having additional shots, and packing with an eye to the Orient. By some miracle, my baggage weighed in at exactly forty pounds.

Leaving my family was quite a wrench. I felt pretty shaky as I walked up the ramp at Logan Airport, in Boston, with a jaunty, *"Sayonara,"* waving at my parents and grandparents. Of course I promised to write often.

My grandmother needn't have worried about my safety. The TWA flight to Los Angeles was smooth as silk. I boned up some more on Japan and by the time I arrived in

Wilmington, California, where we would embark on the SS *Cleveland*, I felt equipped to deal with any emergency. (How wrong can you be!)

The other eight AFSers — four boys, four girls — I met at lunch at The Plush Horse. They came from all over the country, a good-looking, friendly bunch, full of bounce — Peter Martin from Long Island, New York; James Hauhart, Dobbs Ferry, New York; Arthur Lederman, Long Beach, California; David Brudnoy and Katherine Lowry both from Minneapolis; Joyce Stallsmith, Clifton Heights, Pennsylvania; Elizabeth Titus, Syracuse, New York; and Joyce Bartschi, a Mormon from Salt Lake City. She said she had never been on a train, boat or plane before.

My junket to Japan was still a dream until I saw the seven-hundred-passenger liner, its blue and red funnel glistening in the sunshine. Gulls circled noisily overhead as our chaperon distributed our boat tickets and AFS pins and doled out five dollars apiece of our own spending money. We were allowed twenty dollars a month plus forty-nine dollars for souvenirs.

We then gathered around the Director-General of the AFS, a big, husky man with circles of fatigue under his eyes. "If you give everything of yourself," said Mr. Stephen Galatti, winding up his inspiring talk, "you'll have a wonderful time."

We boarded the liner, the girls chirping like sparrows, and headed for our ETC (Economy Tourist Class) accommodations. We five boys shared a dormitory with twenty-seven other males, right over the engines. But we wouldn't have swapped with anyone. Here in steerage we would be meeting the Eastern world — Koreans, Australians, turbaned Hindus, Filipinos and black-robed Chinese.

"All visitors ashore — "

I sprinted up on deck and got tangled in the colored streamers flung by the cheering crowd on the dock. A white-coated steward strode past, banging a gong. The whistle blew a deep, long blast. The ship gradually came alive. There were muffled thuds from below, then rhythmic throbs, as the tugboat pulled us out of the harbor. The colored streamers lengthened, grew taut and finally snapped. The last tie broken! Handkerchiefs fluttered, cheers grew fainter, and the last *"Sayonara"* echoed from ship to shore. We had begun our five-thousand-mile voyage across the Pacific!

The sea was calm, but not me. I had feathers in my stomach at the thought of being cut off from the safe, familiar Western Hemisphere. What adventures and experiences lay ahead? Did Yanks and Asiatics have anything in common? How would I stack up with my Japanese family? Would we be able to understand one another? I'd make mistakes as sure as Tuesday followed Monday.

It wasn't a rough crossing, but some of us were missing at mealtime, Joyce Bartschi frequently. Jimmy didn't mind skipping meals. He was in crew training and counted calories like a fiend. Kate played nurse to Dave, keeping him company while he slumped in his deck chair, green-faced and speechless. The box of saltines at his bedside hadn't done the trick. Coming from a fishing town, I couldn't lose face by being seasick, and I wasn't.

We soon fell into the shipboard routine — deck tennis,

shuffleboard, ping-pong and bingo, at which I lost consistently. All around the clock I'd hear the shouts of Chinese mah-jongg players and kibitzers as chinks struck the board. There was the blaring of the jukebox in the bar, the shrill piping of children, the twang of Filipino guitars, Arthur practicing his fiddle, and the loud-speaker paging us. I always jumped on hearing, "Mr. Peter Bell, Mr. Peter Bell. Please report to the purser's office!"

Throughout the fourteen-day voyage we were the center of attraction. Everybody was curious about the AFS, and we were proud to tell them what a wonderful organization we represented. I had some stimulating talks with Mormon missionaries and serious discussions with an Indian scholar from Madras, who read me his Ph.D. thesis about the influence of the West on India.

In fact, I made friends with people from all over the Near and Middle East. I learned a great deal about my own country from a Filipino Methodist minister, who looked forty and was actually sixty-seven. He was returning from the States — a trip that wiped out his life savings. In his enthusiasm he began writing a book on America — how our country had helped his people to achieve democracy, education and higher standards of living all within a couple of decades. He stirred up something in me, making me realize that "America, the land of opportunity" was more than just a slogan.

Maybe after seeing Japan I'd come to appreciate my own country more. We had been warned not to expect comforts and luxuries. That warning was echoed in our briefings, held each afternoon. AFS restrictions included wear-

9

ing loud shirts or too much lipstick, driving a scooter or car, and straying from our group or host family. We were reminded that the success of our summer depended on our ability to adapt ourselves to foreign customs.

"Don't measure Japan by the Western yardstick," we were told. "Many families make great sacrifices to feed and house you. Appreciate the things they do for you by showing interest. Exercise your feelers. Discuss problems with them or with your chaperon. Remember, your way isn't necessarily the right or better way. It's up to *you* to do the adjusting. Avoid comparisons. Find out the *why* of a social custom or political situation. That will make your trip more meaningful. First and foremost, learn the language!"

These orientation meetings put us on our mettle. Each morning we gathered in the first-class lounge for language lessons. Our instructor, Professor Ichiro Nishizaki, had taught Japanese Lit at the University of California, and he was excellent. I now had a vocabulary of about a hundred words and was sure I'd get along. Silly boy!

On June 20 I was waked at two-thirty A.M. by wild cries of "Hawaii!" I was too bushed to do more than grunt and roll over. Anyhow it proved a false alarm. Shortly after five o'clock, the fellows roused me again. This time I got up, groggy as a clobbered mackerel, and saw the sun rise over Oahu, getting a superb view of Diamond Head. A fellow passenger made arrangements for our stopover at Honolulu, where we spent an unforgettable day.

It began at the pier, where swarms of beautiful girls greeted us with floral *leis*. With every *lei* came a kiss. I bore up bravely under this hoopla, feeling reasonably sure that Japanese girls wouldn't be so generous. Then we were taken on a whirlwind tour of Oahu in an eight-door taxi, hitting all the high spots. After a delicious lunch at the Reef Hotel in Honolulu, we got terrific sunburns on Waikiki Beach, skimming along the surf on an outrigger.

Hawaii was a paradise in technicolor. Our eyes popped at the gigantic flowers and lush vegetation, and our cameras clicked like mad. Whenever it rained with the sun shining, our guide told us, the people would say whimsically, "We're having a little liquid sunshine!" Everybody looked happy. Here was the world's best showcase of integration, all races living in harmony.

Leaving that Garden of Eden was the only sad part. But after tossing our *leis* into the sea (we held on to the colored streamers as long as possible), we consoled ourselves with the thought that we'd be back in two months. That evening I stood on the upper deck, watching Honolulu fade into the distance while a gentle breeze caressed my face. If that sounds mushy — well, *gomen nasai!*

II
RED CARPET TREATMENT

"Welcome to Japan!"

Those three English words coming from the little knot of Japanese at the Yokohama dock on June 29 were music to our ears. Our foster families and friends were a heart-warming sight. While they stood in the early morning mist, trying to identify us from newspaper photographs, I searched their faces for my foster mother. Was she the only lady wearing a kimono?

I waved tentatively and when she waved back, my heart lurched. She stood out from the rest of the group like an exotic butterfly. And that boy beside her must be Kozo. He looked like a little train conductor in his dark blue school uniform.

"Take off your glasses, Dave Brudnoy, so we can see you!" This from a slim Japanese girl in a green sweater, evidently an AFS returnee back from the States.

"Why should I?" Our lanky six-footer made a megaphone of his hands. "I can see *you* all right."

"Dave never takes them off," I shouted. "Even wears them to bed."

"Where are the geisha girls?" Arthur looked crestfallen.

His words were drowned out by the loud-speaker bellowing, "Passengers are requested to check their baggage and all necessary papers."

We trundled into the lounge, all of us keyed up to high G. My first glimpse of Yokohama harbor was a letdown. Except for a few transports and barges, it looked like a great big Gloucester. The sky was overcast and I smelled rain in the air. But nothing could dampen our spirits. Hours before the SS *Cleveland* dropped anchor, at eight A.M., we had been up and champing like race horses. Since we were the first AFSers in the Orient, we were treated like VIP's. For over an hour we had been quizzed and photographed by the *Asahi Evening News*, and welcomed by a representative of the Minister of Education.

When the big moment arrived and we walked down the gangplank, Arthur said sternly, "Let's put our best foot forward, for the sake of the AFS. No monkey business. Act our age."

He meant Dave, who was apt to get out of line. I felt like a seasoned traveler, my raincoat with the germ-proof lining slung over one shoulder, camera and binoculars over the other. But by the time I stepped up to the Okajimas I was as jittery as a bridegroom.

"Mistah Peta Beru?" A dapper little man with a big smile introduced himself as a colleague of Mr. Okajima. "This is to be your famiry."

I bowed and smiled, towering above them. They bowed

in unison, beaming. My foster mother was a petite, gracious-looking woman of about fifty, with dainty hands and feet. She gave me, the tongue-tied American boy, a searching glance. Then I caught a twinkle behind her rimless eyeglasses and began to relax. It was a case of love at first sight. She was a lady in every sense of the word.

"The honorable Okajima-san ask you prease go with Kozo," said the interpreter. "She see you rater at home, yiss?"

After more bows (this time we almost bumped heads), Mrs. Okajima drew some coins from her sleeve and gave them to Kozo. (Lesson Number One: Japanese ladies don't usually carry pocketbooks.) He had been sizing me up like a cocky bantam, his black eyes as defiant as his hair. Perhaps it was just shyness, but he seemed rather blasé. He'd be a tough nut to crack.

When I introduced him to the other AFSers he bowed eight times, solemn as a pallbearer, then accompanied us through customs. Our party had swelled to about thirty, reporters and cameramen sticking to us like flypaper. We taxied to the railway station and boarded a narrow-gauge interurban for Tokyo, about half an hour's ride. Kozo sat beside me, fanning himself.

"*Atsui-ne,*" he said in a surprisingly guttural voice, fiddling with the brass buttons of his tunic.

I nodded, assuming that meant "hot, isn't it?" Why didn't he practice his English on me? He had had three years of it, so his letter said, and I was bursting with questions. "I'm so thrilled to be here, Kozo. It's wonderful of your people to invite me. I hope you'll have time to show me around. There's Kamakura, for instance. Isn't that where you see the world's second largest Buddha?"

"*Yie, so desu.*" His eyes gleamed.

No, it is? What kind of gobbledegook was he handing me? I found out later that saying no when they mean yes was just a polite custom of agreeing with you.

I tried again. "Kamakura is near Yokohama — "

"*Sa?*" He scratched his head. "*Tabun.*"

Maybe. At that I gave up. It was like trying to talk through a plate glass. (Lesson Number Two: Never expect a direct answer in Japan.)

We were both relieved when the train slid into Tokyo Station — a massive, European-style structure with lots of gingerbread. Rai Watanabe, chairman of the AFS Japan Central Committee, had invited us to lunch, and a fleet of cabs streaked off for the restaurant. I soon saw why the midget taxi Kozo and I shared was nicknamed *kamikaze*, meaning suicide. Once the spacious Plaza was left behind and we were caught in a maelstrom of traffic, our cabby went crazy. Never have I seen such reckless driving or heard such incessant horn-blowing. It was terrifying. I felt as though I were tossed into a gigantic mixmaster of wildly careening jeeps, scooters and three-wheeled trucks. Each driver seemed to compete with the next one in scoring near-misses.

As for Tokyo, far from being colorful or exotic, the world's largest city was a roaring, rattling metropolis that put even New York City in the shade. A flash glimpse re-

15

vealed a jumble of Oriental and Western-style buildings, bright orange mailboxes, and people wearing mostly Western garb.

We had stopped at a traffic light and I was speculating about the high accident rate when I heard the screech of brakes and a strangled cry. A *kamikaze* zoomed off, leaving a young schoolboy lying motionless in the street. What floored me was the indifference of pedestrians. They went blithely on their way, insensible to the accident. Where was Japan's far-famed courtesy? Not a single person stopped to see if that boy was hurt badly — until a tall G.I. with Oriental features sprang forward and bent over the victim.

"Oi, oi!" the traffic cop yelled from his cage. He strode over, whipping out a notebook and gesticulating like some Gilbert and Sullivan character. There followed a heated argument, the G.I. shouting angrily in mixed English and Japanese.

I felt strangely drawn to the good-looking Nisei. As our cab shot away, I wondered if he'd be thrown in jail. And was that poor kid badly hurt? "You certainly have a big traffic problem here," I said, hoping that Kozo would explain the whole enigma.

He shrugged and said blandly, *"Hai, hai."*

Yes, yes, was all he had to say. By the time we reached the Japanese-American restaurant, my head was splitting. I watched Kozo floundering with the heavy silverware. We had got off to a bad start, but I mustn't let it show. During lunch the reporters recorded our comments on tape, and I was tempted to ask about public heartlessness, but decided to suspend judgment.

16

They snapped more pictures, then distributed copies of the *Asahi Evening News* (Japan's largest English newspaper) with our faces splashed across the front page. The speed with which news travels in the Orient — five hours after being interviewed! The fact that the copy had been flown from ship by carrier pigeons gave us a big charge.

"See you all at the next orientation meeting," I said in something of a panic, as our group left for temporary quarters near Tokyo. In the next few days, I couldn't expect to run across one American or hear one completed English sentence. It made me feel sort of orphaned.

"Come, prease." Kozo led me to a green Plymouth sedan, where a liveried chauffeur bowed and took my luggage. The car started out for Nishi-Ogikubo, on the western outskirts of Tokyo. I was naturally anxious to meet Mr. Okajima, but when I said something to that effect Kozo began, "*Ano-ne* — " Then, struggling with English, he explained that his father spent half the time in Osaka, where he was managing director of the Mitsubishi Shipbuilding and Engineering Company. Kozo's second older brother lived in Osaka, the eldest one in Tokyo.

We had come to a nice residential neighborhood of small houses, concrete or unpainted wood, and fenced in by shrubbery, cypress trees or bamboo. The chauffeur carried my luggage through a gray gate and into a tiny hall. There, on a concrete square, we left our shoes among an assortment of footgear, umbrellas and old-fashioned shoehorns. Then, from a higher teakwood level, Kozo opened a sliding paper door, fragile as eggshell, and we entered a large, oblong room off the long corridor, walking on rectangles of black-bordered *tatami* — straw matting.

The Formal Room took me by surprise. It had the austere, orderly gleam of a museum. There were no chairs, sofas, bookshelves or knicknacks — only a low, black-lacquered table and a beautifully carved lowboy inlaid with mother-of-pearl. The focal point was the *tokonoma,* or alcove of honor, the arched wall recess outlined by a highly polished cherry-tree trunk. A single white peony decorated the low dais, and on the wall a picture scroll of Mount Fuji. At the right of this *kakemono* I saw a built-in cupboard crowned by a wood carving of Chinese characters. Kozo translated the words — "To make the world more wonderful," adding that this was his mother's motto.

I stood lost in admiration as Mrs. Okajima came in, smiling and taking the short, sliding steps of kimono-wearers. She had changed her *zōri* or straw sandals for *tabi,* white socks that looked more like mittens, with a separate place for the big toe. Her rich yellow kimono made a splash of color in the restful room. (Lesson Number Three: Simplicity is the keynote of Japanese homes. It is the occupants who provide the décor.)

I knew it wasn't easy for these reserved people to have strangers living in their home, and I heard later that Mrs. Okajima had qualms about taking in an American boy. I didn't know how to express my gratitude. The silence that fell made only me uneasy. *They* didn't seem to mind. The Nipponese aren't afraid of silence. They can spend a whole evening among friends without saying a word.

"We have seven rooms," said Kozo with a shy grin. "I

show you rater." His choppy staccato reminded me a little of American Indians. "Now, prease, your room."

As he led the way upstairs, I ducked my head to avoid the ceiling and electric lights. Mine was the best room at the back of the house. It overlooked the garden, which was invisible at the moment, the oil-paper windows and shutters being closed. The only furniture I could see was a tiny bureau or *tansu*. What would I sleep on? Where was the *futon?*

While I unpacked, Mrs. Okajima brought me a *yukata*, a blue and white cotton garment with a green sash or *obi*. "For wear in house," Kozo explained. "After bazz." As temporary head of the house, he played host with great relish. I was bowled over and mumbled *"Domo arigato gozai-masu,"* hastily fishing out my presents — hand-printed place mats and napkins with the Folly Cove design. She surprised me by saying, "Beautiful," in English. We exchanged more bows — formalities repeated with Kozo, for whom I had brought a tie clip with the Gloucester fisherman-at-the-wheel seal.

I had always thought my manners pretty fair, but I'll never brag about them again. My face was cracking with the strain of matching Oriental smiles.

"Haru-san say bazz ready." And Kozo added, *"O-furo* downstair."

Haru-san must be the maid. *O-furo*, I knew, meant bath. I trailed my foster brother downstairs where we undressed in an anteroom. We then walked through a sliding door of frosted glass into a steam-filled room with two levels. The lower one, of cement, had a wooden drainboard and on this we squatted, sloshing ourselves, scrubbing each other's back and rinsing off the soap. (Most important!) I was thankful that the maid, the official back-scrubber, didn't show up.

As Honorable Guest, I was *ichi ban* (number one) in the tub. This barrel-shaped vessel had a built-in charcoal stove, keeping the water at 110 degrees. Kozo advised me to submerge quickly, then sit absolutely motionless. I held my breath and sank into the scalding water, he adjusted the wooden cover so the heat (and I) couldn't escape, and there I hunched, jackknifed for a long time, soaking and meditating.

When I got out, I could only think of a boiled lobster. I looked like one, too. But it was wonderfully invigorating. The whole ritual took about forty-five minutes. Question: When is the rinsing water changed?

III
HOME WAS NEVER
LIKE THIS

I went down to dinner that evening feeling silly in my *yukata*. When the maid appeared, barefooted, I nearly dropped the bars of Maine pine-scented soap I had brought her. She fell to her knees and kissed the floor. I could hardly keep a straight face. What a bang our own maid, Ruby, would get out of that!

Haru-san — she must have been in her early twenties — wore a red and white checked gingham dress and apron, her head bound in a white kerchief. She was quaint and demure, her almond-shaped eyes brimming over with fun and curiosity. We clicked at once. Overwhelmed by my modest little gift, she blushed, smiled and chirped, *"Domo arigato gozaimasu!"* Then she slid back the cupboard door and took out three square silken cushions (*zabuton*), placing them around the low table. As guest of honor I sat with my back to the *tokonoma*, but my legs refused to fold properly and I felt like a kid playing mumblety-peg.

Haru-san gave us each a moist cloth called *O-shibori*. What for? Why, to wash our faces and hands, of course! As the weather grew colder, I learned, those cloths became hotter. At the moment my blazing face could stand a cooling off. (Lesson Number Four: The Japanese don't use napkins *or* place mats.) Dinner began with a delicious bean-curd soup, which we drank out of dainty porcelain bowls. Japanese food is calculated to please the eye as well as the palate. Kozo said his mother had carved the highly waxed, leaf-shaped platters of cedarwood. They were exquisite.

The second course wouldn't go down my gullet until I practically drowned those thin slices of raw fish in soy sauce. I didn't dare raise my eyes from the table.

The main course, *sukiyaki*, was a scrumptious meat and vegetable dish, and with it came rice and various other things. My clumsiness with chopsticks (*hashi*) brought a smile, grin and giggle from Mrs. Okajima, Kozo, and Haru-san respectively. For dessert we had *O-kashi*, sweet soy-bean cakes, and green tea, the water heated in a shiny copper kettle hung over a *hibachi* or charcoal brazier.

With the help of dictionaries and the sign language we managed to communicate fairly well, Kozo interpreting his mother's remarks. I learned that Operation Soup began with the *tofu* man calling at the back door and slicing the sweet, spongy soybean cake he carried in see-saw baskets. Rice was cooked, without salt, in a wooden kettle placed inside an iron one. Everything in the *sukiyaki* had to be sliced very fine — beef, scallions, bamboo shoots, spring onions, watercress, Chinese cabbage, mushrooms, seaweed and bean curd.

It was cooked in soy sauce with sugar and chicken broth.

"*Okā-san* cook any ranguage." Kozo said proudly. But his manner toward his mother was casual and offhand, and he snickered when I rose, bowed and said politely in Japanese, "The meal was well prepared." Obviously he was a "new-thinking" youth with no patience for the whole rigmarole of honorifics.

I was to find Mrs. Okajima a very accomplished lady. Besides doing wood carvings, she played the *samisen* (a banjolike instrument), did beautiful embroidery, performed the tea ceremony (which left Kozo cold), and made geisha dolls — fascinating figures about a foot high — dressed in rich brocade. With all her talents she still took lessons in music and calligraphy.

Her flower arrangements were superb. Apparently there are about three hundred different schools, although the basic principle is the same whether you have three or more flowers or blossoming branches. The longest one, symbolizing Heaven, always goes in the middle, the shortest one (Earth) at the left, and the one of medium height (Man) at the right. Each flower personified some virtue. Lotus blossoms stood for purity, wistaria for gentleness; cherry blossoms symbolized the ideals of the old samurai or military class.

The traditional place for flower arrangements was the *tokonoma*. That picture scroll above the dais was only one of many *kakemono* the Okajimas owned. The rest were kept in the cupboard, only one being shown at a time.

"We keep change so never get tired see same picture," said Kozo.

"A sensible idea, rotating them. Like our art-lending library system," which I described.

I had made the mistake of letting him see a snapshot of our house in Gloucester. It had impressed him terrifically. "Wounderful! *Takusan* — very much *ooki*, beeg, *ne?*" He kept apologizing for the size of his family's house while showing me around.

Besides the two rooms upstairs, which he and I occupied, there were five below. When he said there were seven, he didn't count the kitchen, bathroom or maid's room. I had Mrs. Okajima's room. She would sleep in The Formal Room. Japanese ingenuity converts any room into several small ones by adjusting the paper-paneled walls that slide on grooved tracks. At the left of the long corridor bisecting the house was the toilet (*benjo*), Haru-san's room (a little cubicle where she did all her mending and ironing), the washroom, bath and kitchen.

Kozo marched me past that small, dark kitchen, done in natural wood like the rest of the house. A guest must never see the kitchen. Haru-san herself refused to let me in, but one day when I was alone in the house I peeped. Except for a refrigerator, everything looked medieval — the iron sink with the cold-water tap, the crude wooden chopping block, the tiny portable oil stove, the utensils and implements. No handy cake-mixes here, no blenders or juice-extractors or other gadgets that we consider necessities! The average American maid would have walked out on such primitive arrangements.

Next to the kitchen was a small "informal" dining room, and beyond that a den, where we were to spend most of

Okajima Family

Dinner at Home

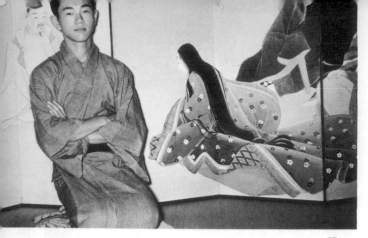

Kozo

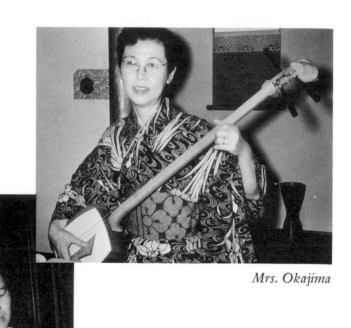

Mrs. Okajima

Haru-san

our evenings. The Okajimas had never slept in beds or bathed in anything but wooden tubs. They had no central heating, no plumbing or electric stove, but they did own a television set. It stood in the corner like an upstart. Beside this twentieth-century idol was an ancient one — a *butsudan*, or tiny Buddhist altar, built in the wall.

"*Okā-san* pray here," said Kozo. "But no me." He grinned and looked abashed. "Kozo *dame* — bad. Now you see garden." He slid back a paper panel, exposing a pocket-sized garden. It contained a large crimson dahlia, an azalea bush, a hand pump and a little doghouse.

It stumped me. Japanese gardens, I had heard, were poet's dreams — miniature bridges and stone lanterns, dwarfed pines, mossy carpets, with goldfish ponds or springs trickling over curiously shaped stones. I was amused at the tiny patch of manicured lawn, which Kozo said Haru-san kept trimmed with scissors so that her master, a golf enthusiast, could practice putting shots. Mr. Okajima knocked the balls into a canvas bag, hung on a gatepost.

Near a large flat rock, reserved for parking *geta* or wooden shoes, was the doghouse. Kozo introduced me to the little white pooch poking her muzzle through the hole. "Parl." This was Pearl's permanent residence — or prison, since she wasn't allowed in the house. A narrow teakwood walk or gallery ran from the den past the Formal Room and to the Western Room (about which more later).

We spent the rest of the evening in the den, watching the nine-thirty news program — a national TV hook-up showing us AFSers romping on shipboard. A weird experience, seeing yourself on TV! One shot highlighted Joyce

Bartschi trying to answer a barrage of questions on deck and Pete Martin breaking in impatiently, "How can you say what you think of Japan before you've seen it?" Another shot had us in the lounge exchanging dollars for yen. When Jimmy held out a ten-yen coin, asking what he could buy with it, a Nisei onlooker said, shrugging, "Not much, with three hundred and fifty yen to the dollar!"

My foster mother watched it all with an air of bright expectancy, not understanding a word. She laughed at Arthur's clowning, however, until her eyes were mere slits of mirth, and somehow that brought us closer together. Words were unnecessary. When she lit a cigarette, I did a double take. In all other respects she seemed so old-worldish, like a lady in a Japanese print.

After a nightcap of hot *sake* — rice wine a little like sauterne — I was ready for bed. I unfolded my cramped legs, rose, bowed and said, "*Ohayo gozaimasu!*" When Kozo burst out laughing, I wondered if I'd boggled. I bolted upstairs, grabbed my dictionary and found I *had* got my wires crossed. I should have said, "*Oyasumi nasai.*" Oh well, at least my ill-timed "good morning" broke the ice with him.

Haru-san had unrolled the *futon*, apparently kept in the cupboard, and over it she had erected a green mosquito tent. It was hot as blazes, but the windows had to remain shut as a precaution against burglars — and insects. When I saw a paper fan in that snug little *kaya*, and a reading lamp, I was so touched I wanted to rush downstairs and hug her. But that just wasn't done in Japan.

Too tired to write in my diary, I stripped and stretched out on my *futon*. It was quite comfortable, and such a practical idea, too! No baby ever falls out of bed in Japan. My pillow felt like a beanbag — a cylinder stuffed with bran, oats or rice hulls — I don't know which. I lay there drowsily, listening to the patter of rain on the roof, the click-clack of *geta* on the pavement, and some bell-ringer going through the streets, sounding very romantic.

Everything seemed strange and different in this topsy-turvy land — the language, customs, people. Their callousness about that street accident baffled me. In spite of Mrs. Okajima's warmth and kindness, I felt like an alien and — well, let's face it, I was homesick.

IV
SUNDAY IN TOKYO

"Peetah-san?" A gentle voice woke me out of a deep sleep. "*Ohayo gozaimasu!*"

I peered through the mosquito tent, croaking good morning. There was Haru-san, a smile on her round, peasant face, curtsying and kissing the floor. It was beginning all over again! She slid back the paper windows, opened the wooden shutters, made another curtsy and vanished noiselessly, murmuring, "*Asa-gohan.*"

Asa-gohan? Oh yes, breakfast. *Gohan* was cooked rice. I crawled out of my tent and looked through the window, hoping to see Honorable Fuji-san. But the snow-capped volcano was invisible on this cloudy Sunday morning. As I slipped on my *yukata*, I remembered hearing that Tokyo people during the American Occupation said you could see two famous sights on a clear day — Fuji and MacArthur.

"*Ohayo.*" Kozo entered, yawning, his black and white *yukata* as rumpled as his hair. When he saw my red belt, his eyes glinted. "Beautiful, *ne?*" He stroked it tenderly.

Apparently he was something of a dandy, with a flair for bright colors. (In Japan red is a girl's color.)

On our way down to the washroom, I asked him if I couldn't skip the bows and fancy stuff with Haru-san. "*Hai, hai*," he said crisply, "Enough you say *ohayo*. No bowings." What a relief!

We found Mrs. Okajima kneeling at the low table in the "informal" dining room. Like most Japanese, she was an early riser. She smiled, bowed and bade me good morning, then went into peals of laughter when I said good night, just to let her know I had discovered my mistake.

Breakfast was big enough for a lumberjack — bean-curd soup, two eggs, toast, coleslaw, thin slices of pork, rice and green tea. Kozo picked up the *Asahi Shimbun* and began reading from right to left, after remarking casually that his mother had ordered the English *Asahi* delivered for my benefit. My thank-you sounded very inadequate.

When the phone rang, he darted into the corridor and I heard him bark, "*Moshi, moshi*" (hello, hello). There followed a rapid spate of Japanese. Then, "Yep, yep, so rong!" He came back, beaming like Puck. "Watanabe-san meet us Meiji Jingu Shrine two o'crock. Okay?"

"Fine." I was to see a bit of the old and new Japan — a Shinto Shrine and a jazz show. Discussing the day's plans was a tough job. Mrs. Okajima was humble and painstaking about learning English. She pored over her dictionary with knitted brow, bringing out each word with an apologetic little laugh.

As we left the house later on, Haru-san fetched my cap, brushed off an invisible fleck of dust, placed it on my head and gave it an affectionate pat. Talk about service! I felt like a child packed off to kindergarten. We started for the interurban station, a few minutes' walk away. Directly across the street was a radio and electrical supply shop with a sign in Japanese characters as decorative as a *kakemono*. Brightly colored *futons* were airing from windows and bamboo fences. Whenever a snazzy car whizzed by, Kozo would ask, "Many beeg cahs in America?" Anything American was catnip to him.

Along the main street of Nishi-Ogikubo a loud speaker blared, "Love Me Tender." As sung by a Japanese crooner it came out, "Rub Me Tender." Kozo jiggled and snapped his fingers. He knew all the current hits and like most teenagers was a rabid "fan of jazz" — one American importation Japanese parents strongly disapprove of.

The jingle of slot machines coming from a *pachinko* parlor stopped him in his tracks. "We go in, *ne?* Maybe we win!"

"Okay." I didn't know then that students were forbidden to gamble.

We had to push our way to a slot machine, after buying seven steel balls for a few yen. These parlors, Kozo said, were packed from morning till night, even women succumbing to the lure of pinballs going *pa-CHIN-ko*. The prizes were staples like sugar and canned food, the cans valued more than the contents, as metal is so scarce in Japan. Alas, we had no luck!

"My brozzer all time rucky," Kozo said wistfully, on leaving. "You have *pachinko* in Groucester?" When I said no, he looked astounded. "But *pachinko* come from America, *ne?*" I nodded, explaining that slot machines were illegal in Massachusetts.

Getting into the train was another free-for-all. Away from home the Japanese revert to normal human beings, pushing, jostling and shoving just like Americans. It's the old heave-ho and every man for himself. Since I'm a head taller than most Nipponese, I could at least breathe in that stuffy, crowded interurban.

A short walk from Harjuku Station brought us to the Meiji Shrine. You might call it a small city in itself. The precincts embrace some one hundred and seventy-nine acres and include a sports arena and a museum besides various religious edifices. While we waited for Rai, I noticed teen-age girls, mostly in stateside suits and Italian haircuts, walking alongside their boy friends, whereas older women in kimonos paddled respectfully behind their menfolk. Usually Mama-san had a child on each side and a baby slung on her back — a china doll with a sleepy smile. The older the woman, the more somber her kimono.

The G.I.'s sauntering by made me think of that Nisei I had seen yesterday. His face haunted me. I couldn't get him out of my mind. I made a mental note to ask Rai about pedestrian reaction to street accidents. But not today, with Kozo present.

"Hi, Pete! Hi, Kozo!" Rai, clad in khaki trousers and yellow T shirt, hailed us with a broad grin. You'd never know from his casual dress or manner that he was a big wheel. "You're treading on holy ground," he said with a clipped Oxford accent, gripping my hand like a blacksmith. "This is where the late Empress Meiji used to walk." He was a human dynamo with tremendous vitality and an excellent brain. He had what Dave called "animal charm" plus devilish eyes like Kozo. Both were rebels.

It was wonderful to hear real English again. Rai was a returnee who had spent a year in Dearborn, Michigan, and was now attending Tokyo University. I bombarded him with questions as we mingled with the Sunday throngs and "viewed" the water lotuses and irises. There were more than eighty varieties of irises, flowering like a rainbow river through the shrine precincts.

I was fascinated by the trees, especially the *bonsai* — full-grown miniature trees two hundred years old, perfectly proportioned and yet some of them only a foot high. Each tree was labeled — cherry, maple, cypress, Chinese juniper, and Japanese cedar, these cryptomerias as old and beautiful as our California redwoods.

We passed through two *torii* — open gates like goalposts marking the entrance to a shrine. The second one was about forty feet high and of natural wood, as was the shrine itself.

"Most Shinto shrines are like this one, plain and austere," Rai said, as I photographed it. "But the gateway to the Toshogu Shrine in Nikko is the most elaborate and beautiful in the world. Kozo must take you to see it."

"*Hai, hai,*" and my foster brother said something Rai translated. "We have a proverb, 'Unless you've seen Nikko you can't say *kekko.*' *Kekko* means splendid."

"I'll have to learn more about Japanese religion," I said, while we sipped hot tea, served free, under a cryptomeria.

Rai raked his high black pompadour. "So you want to know about the opiate of the people," he said in a bantering tone. "Well, we have three religions — Shintoism, Buddhism and Christianity. Shintoism's really a cult. It glorifies cleanliness, ancestor worship and patriotism. The 'splendid Japanese,' you know. It goes in for faith-healing and magic and holds all nature to be divine — rocks, trees, mountains . . ."

My attention strayed to a middle-aged, bespectacled Japanese hovering nearby. What was he after?

"There are about eight hundred million *kami*," Rai went on dryly. "Take the kitchen god. Kojin Sama has three faces, six hands and a hideous expression, to frighten away devils and prevent domestic disasters."

"Such superstitions in this modern, scientific age?"

"I don't wonder you're incredulous, Pete. Superstitions hang around our necks like millstones. MacArthur abolished Shintoism as a national religion, but you'll see shrines all over Japan, even on top of Mount Fuji. The average Japanese gets married at a Shinto shrine and buried by a Buddhist priest. Shintoism helps you get through this life, Buddhism prepares you for the hereafter. Reincarnation, you know."

"How can you belong to two religions?"

"Why not?" Rai shugged. "It's double insurance. Some people are Christians, too. Christians are an influential minority, with twenty-four different sects here. They operate twenty-two universities."

"My parents onry Buddhist," Kozo tugged at his large, flyaway ears. "Me nozzing."

"Kozo's an agnostic. He doesn't know what he believes." Rai drained his teacup. "He's all mixed up, the way most of his generation is. We're living in two different centuries."

"In a hundred 'ear we same as America," Kozo said, grinning.

I smiled, then gave that stranger a sharp glance, wondering if he was a bunko artist. "I can understand why Japanese teen-agers should be mixed up." I had religious doubts myself. My mother, a Protestant, went to a Universalist church, while my father was a nature-worshipper. He was "taking us to church" when he drove us to the Audubon Botanical Gardens on Sundays.

"Lots of apartment houses going up now omit the *butsu-dan*," Rai was saying. "Another sign that Buddhism is losing favor. It's mostly a show for our young people. Wish I could believe in some faith. Of course," he added with a faint smile, "I'd probably pray if I were hard-pressed."

At this point the stranger approached with a formal bow and handed me his card. "Pardon me for intruding, but I'm always interested when I hear English. I am Principal of the Shigakukan English Institute in Tokyo, and I would be most grateful for your name and address so that my pupils can write you. It would be a splendid way of improving their English."

His English needed no improving! "Of course," I said, ashamed of my suspicions.

After he left, Rai grinned and warned me that we AFSers would be mobbed all summer long by strangers. "Our people are crazy to learn English." He glanced at his watch. "We've still got time for a swim before the jazz show at the Koma comes on. Jingu Pool isn't far from here. Are you game?"

34

It was an enormous pool, open to the sky but walled in with bleachers all around. We stripped in the men's locker, Kozo placing my clothes carefully on top of our bin. Divers were doing spectacular stunts from eight boards of varying heights. One pair clasped each other's neck and ankles, taking off for a thirty-five-foot plunge. Then eight divers hit the water in perfect unison. I wouldn't have missed it for the world. It was a pleasure to watch those slim, bronze bodies, lithe as panthers. I was to see few overweight or white-haired people — here or elsewhere in Japan.

Between dips we sat on the rim of the pool, legs dangling. I told Rai about my first Japanese bath and how scared I had been that Haru-san would turn up.

He laughed. "But that's partly what maids are for. Our 'Turkish' baths all hire Japanese girls. Ordinary bathhouses have male backwashers."

Kozo said he couldn't understand the way Americans bathe. "How you get clean rinsing in same water you wash?"

"You have a point. But is the rinsing water ever changed?"

"Sure, every day," Rai said. "Might get murky of course if you're the last one of a dozen or more. That's why the lord and master always goes first. After him comes the eldest son and younger boys, next the mother, eldest daughter and other girls. The maid is last, naturally."

Naturally. Poor Haru-san! So the Order of the Bath was part and symbol of the whole social hierarchy! Once Mr. Okajima was home, I'd be demoted. I kept speculating about him. Was he as nice as Mrs. Okajima?

35

The young people at Jingu impressed me with their correct behavior. There was no handholding or any of the easy familiarity you saw in America. And yet the Japanese thought nothing of mixed nude bathing.

"Well, Pete," said Rai, when I put this inconsistency up to him, "there's nothing shocking about nakedness to the older generation. They couldn't see why MacArthur clamped down on that ancient custom. What does offend us is any display of emotion in public. Naked hearts and minds. Any form of physical intimacy, we feel, is in bad taste. Until the war, kisses and clinches were cut out of American films. Have you seen any kissing here, except between mothers and babies perhaps?"

"So far no. Only the floor." I smiled, thinking of Harusan. What was it that Lafcadio Hearn wrote about the Japanese? "They never rush into each other's arms or utter phrases of affection, but show their love through acts of exquisite courtesy and kindness."

"Americans have saying, 'Wear heart on elbow,' *ne?*"

"Sleeve, Kozo." I had offered to teach him to dance and he had refused. I now realized why that would be dangerous. High school students were allowed only folk or square dancing. And yet before that Sunday came to an end I was to see an exhibition of abandon that eclipsed any American spectacle.

It happened at Koma Stadium, an ultramodern theater rather like Manhattan's Radio Center Music Hall. This was the opening week and we were lucky to get in. Queues stretched for three blocks. The walls of the foyer, swallowing up a third of the building, were spattered with flamboyant posters of stars. Most of the two thousand jazz fans were youths — boys with shaggy-bear haircuts and bobby-soxers in tight sweaters and blue jeans. I saw many pony tails but no pigtails.

Six top bands gave us an imitation of American jazz on a revolving stage, drums keeping up a perpetual barrage. Between numbers, chorines in ballet costumes did a ring-around-the-rosy. It was badly synchronized. Periodically, one girl or another would lose her grip and go spinning into the wings. But the scenery and costumes were really terrific.

So were the crooners, who sported violent blues, reds and greens. They sang a mixture of rock 'n' roll and hillbilly (rockabilly), writhing and gyrating in lunatic fashion. "Bebop A-lula," "Just Walkin' in the Rain" — the English lyrics meant nothing to them. But the effect was atomic. Sedate-looking girls, whom you'd ordinarily associate with flower arrangements and the tea ceremony, seemed absolutely bewitched. The audience went wild. They screamed, whistled, swayed to the rhythm of the music, clicked flashlight bulbs, stamped their feet and threw confetti across the footlights. One girl even swooned.

In all the pandemonium Kozo astonished me most. Rockabilly had uncorked him. He snapped his fingers, rolled his eyes and shimmied like a pressure cooker.

I grinned at Rai and said slyly, "So the Japanese never show any emotion!"

He looked disgusted. "This is one of the bad effects of the movies. Do you know the 3-S policy in colonialism? Screen, sex and sports."

37

V

BULL SESSION

"We've been in Japan only a few days," Arthur Lederman began gingerly, as we AFSers sat around the big table in Tokyo's International House facing several Japanese returnees and half a dozen reporters. "But we've already noticed that courtesy seems to be left at home."

"And there's little gallantry even there," chimed in Elizabeth Titus, demure in a blue jumper. "I suppose we're pampered and spoiled, but Japanese men seem so different — overbearing. It's hard to get used to the husband being the center of the household."

"Oh come on, why not admit it, Japanese manners and morals are both fascinating and appalling!" Dave's sun goggles swiveled from Arthur to Liz and, ignoring the raised eyebrows and muffled comments, he went ahead brashly, "In social matters the Japanese is unmatched in politeness. Behind the wheel of a car he's a maniac. On foot he's a fool, crossing against signals, barely moving an inch to avoid a *kamikaze*."

At Home in Japan

Learning a New Way of Life

The first orientation meeting had come to order (or disorder). The *Asahi Evening News* had given us a fine lunch, so this was a case of biting the hand that fed us. But Rai, our moderator, kept saying stoutly, "Fire away. We can take it!"

His foster brother, Pete Martin, didn't believe that Japanese politeness was artificial. "We must consider both sides of the personalities, public and private. I suppose living in cities develops more of a Western personality."

"Is it part of Western personality to hog seats in busses and trains," Dave flared, "while old women stand in the aisle, bent double under bundles and babies?"

That was a ticklish point. Japanese women were always embarrassed when I offered them my seat. They needed a lot of coaxing. "*Should* we give our seats to a lady?" I asked Rai.

"Only to an old woman or a mother with a baby. It's not *shukan* to offer girls seats, although we might well adopt this American custom." He sat with chin in fist, calm and poised. "Tokyo's electric lines now run special coaches giving old people and children top priority. The idea was first called 'ladies' cars.' "

"Why is that necessary?" Dave asked. "Isn't respect for old age ingrained in your culture and religion?"

"Yes, but there are contradictions in our traditions. Furthermore, they clash with democratic ideals. Asiatic women have always been considered inferior to men, and their duty is to obey and serve. That's dinned into a girl's ears from babyhood. All her life she's ruled by the men in the family. When she marries, she transfers her loyalty from father to husband." Rai loosened his collar and picked up a fan. "Our system has its drawbacks, but we are approaching true equality between the sexes."

My thoughts strayed to Haru-san. "Another thing, Rai. The Okajimas have a wonderful maid, but she's just a work-horse. Never gets a day off. Seems a bit stiff."

"The Okajimas are a perfect example of the traditional family, which is gradually dying out in big cities." He grunted. "As a liberal socialist, I'm all for equal rights. You can't deny that the average woman here is much better off today. She doesn't have to eat at second table; she has prop-erty rights; she can travel alone; dress as she pleases and choose her own career and interests."

"That's true," a Japanese returnee spoke up. "My mother has as much say-so about household matters as my father. My sister watches baseball games and does just about ev-erything I do. We have far more freedom than our parents ever had."

"Too much, perhaps," remarked a girl reporter. "Our elders feel that today's young people are getting out of hand. We recently ran an interview with Judge Morita. He said that juvenile delinquency has increased because the family system has broken down. Parents and teachers have lost their authority. Young people now want to live their own 'democratic' way of life." She smiled ruefully. "Re-member how those teen-agers behaved at the Koma last Sunday?"

"I suppose their ancestors would have turned over in their graves — "

"Our dead are usually cremated, Pete," Rai pointed out.

"But teen-agers have rights, too." Kate Lowry was indignant. "It's only natural to want to be independent. Why can't a Japanese girl go out with whomever she likes? My parents don't object to my going steady and they're both doctors."

"Group dating is still the rule," Rai said impassively, "among good high school students."

Was it? Last night, when Kozo took me to Hibiya Park, I saw couples on every bench, pitching woo. What's more, the boys were smoking. If they'd been caught they would have been expelled from school. Group dating was okay in theory but did it work out in practice? "What's behind that custom?" I asked Rai.

"Largely economic reasons. Students haven't the time or the money to spend on girls. In group dating our girls go Dutch. Besides, we can't afford to marry before our middle or late twenties. There's a big gap in Japan between wages and prices, you know. The average Japanese earns roughly fifty-five dollars a month. And that goes for professional people, too. My father gets forty cents a house call."

"But women's wages are even lower than men's." Jim Hauhart looked up from his doodlings. "And girls are still slaves. Your new Constitution forbids selling young girls into geisha houses, but do you really believe that'll stop such an old and well-paying business?"

"I can't say." Rai's smile became strained. "I don't own a crystal ball. Our institutions and traditions are centuries old. You can't expect a complete switch overnight. Give us time. We're making headway. Women can now vote; there are women in the Diet — "

"But opportunities for women are still limited." Across from me sat the international correspondent of the Japan AFS Committee. Pretty, sloe-eyed Yoshiko Sadatoshi, who did all the donkey work. She was invaluable, but she could never take Rai's place as chairman. The AFS would have lost face.

"The war and the Occupation produced changes that our die-hards call earth-shaking," he continued. "Among other things, MacArthur disarmed us and handed us a constitution outlawing war. He organized labor, broke up family cartels, revamped our educational system, gave us a land-reform program and gave women equal civil rights. He also stripped the police force of its power so that now law-breakers have increased alarmingly." Rai's black eyes swept the lot of us. "The fact is, no other country in the world has changed so much or so fast as Japan."

I didn't have a chance to ask him about public indifference to street accidents. The meeting broke up with a buzz of farewells. Six AFSers were scattering to all parts of Japan — Dave to Fujui, where he would live with a Buddhist priest — leaving only Arthur, Pete Martin and myself near Tokyo. I admired the patient, good-natured way Rai and the others had taken our attacks. We had been pretty rough on them, finding fault and criticizing instead of asking the *why* of social customs.

When I jumped off the interurban at Nishi-Ogikubo, it was raining hard, and me without a *Kasa!*

"Peetah-san?"

There was Mrs. Okajima's maid in her housedress and high *geta*, smiling up at me under a large black umbrella.

Poor thing. How long had she been waiting for me? She had no idea when I'd be back.

Haru-san intrigued me. You would have called her a drudge. She worked from morning till night cleaning, cooking, running errands, rubbing and scrubbing backs, and doing everything the hard way. She had no vacuum cleaner, no washing machine, no electric iron. Kimonos were ripped apart each time they were laundered, then sewed together again. I could just see any American maid doing that.

It took me a long time to discover the secret of her contentment. She certainly wasn't overpaid. I was staggered when I found out what she earned. Mrs. Okajima brought up the subject that same evening, as we sat in the den. After a long silence she said timidly, *"Gomen kudasai* — prease excuse, but how much your maid get?"

"I don't know. I think thirty dollars a week."

"So desu-ka?" She looked incredulous. *"Takusan, ne?"*

"Yes, I suppose to you that's a lot."

"O-Haru get sree — " Then, with a helpless laugh, she wrote out thirty-eight hundred yen. Roughly ten dollars a month.

Haru-san had been working for the Okajimas for eight years, ever since she was sixteen. They didn't have to worry about losing her. She was a fixture, part of the family. Her prospects of marriage were dim. She had no friends and little or no recreation, and yet she was as happy as a robin digging worms. This war orphan from southern Japan considered herself lucky to work for a private family. Girls of her class and circumstances were either indentured into a mill or else sold into houses of prostitution.

The more I thought about her, the more I understood the secret of her happiness. Her only ambition was to serve others. She made the word *jochu* (servant) sound like the most beautiful word in any language. I'm sure she never dreamt of taking a trip to Bermuda or becoming a Hollywood star. She asked only to be appreciated. How proud she was when Mrs. Okajima entrusted her with Kozo's little niece, who had been visiting us! Taking that child home to Tokyo gave Haru-san a chance to see the big city. It was the only time I saw her spruced up.

She took pleasure in simple things — watching Kozo and me set off firecrackers. The Okajimas didn't know that *hanabi* meant the Fourth of July to us. I was so busy that I had overlooked Independence Day. Not until I heard a double-header between the Yanks and the Red Sox, over the Far East radio network, did I remember that we had lost a day crossing the international date line.

We were fast becoming celebrities. We had already appeared on six TV programs. The *International Graphic*, a monthly magazine, had taken three of us on a "U.S. Inspection Trip" of Tokyo, subsequently running a picture spread with our comments. (Some of mine were unprintable.) We were constantly interviewed. News reporters would pop up from nowhere, asking me blanket questions: What do you think of Japan? Do you feel at home here? How do you find things?

That last one had me stymied. Yes, how *do* you find things in Tokyo? It practically takes radar. Tokyo proper was divided into twenty-six *ku* or wards (the Okajimas

lived in Suginami-ku), but most streets were unmarked.
Not only that, there was the maddening custom of num-
bering houses as they were built so that No. 52 might be
next to No. 5. You hunted and hunted until you were cross-
eyed.

Most Tokyoites speak a little English — fortunately, as
my Japanese was very wobbly. I would approach strangers
with a set speech: "My name is Peter Bell. Tokyo is very
hot. Now may I have your permission to depart into English?" I kept expecting signs of hostility from our wartime
enemies. The last American troops had only just left Japan. Allied bombs had destroyed four million homes in Tokyo alone. How could the Japanese forget Hiroshima and
Nagasaki? Then, too, in 1954 radioactive fall-out from our
bomb tests had proven deadly to fishermen on the ill-fated
Lucky Dragon. Resentment was only natural, even among
these philosophers and fatalists. And yet I was treated with
the utmost courtesy.

There was only one exception. When I tried to snap two
old men playing chess on a curb, one of them threatened
to throw a pawn at me. So many Japanese love to be photographed that I was baffled until Rai explained later that the
camera is an evil eye to the older generation, robbing you of
your soul. That was news to me.

Simply walking through the streets of Tokyo was an ad-
venture. Everything looked so new and different, I wished
I had a housefly's myriad eyes. This great, sprawling city
of eight and a half million is far from beautiful, but parts
of it are very picturesque. It's crisscrossed with canals,

some of them spanned by arched bridges of red lacquer. The Sumida River flows through Tokyo, emptying into the Bay of Tokyo.

In the heart of the city I came to an old teahouse, the graceful lines and curves of this *ochaya* reflected in the waters of the Sumida. It looked serene and incongruous among all the government and municipal buildings, the foreign embassies and the hotels. I was struck by the contrast between ancient and modern. Street venders, bent under loaded baskets, trotted barefoot beside nattily dressed gentlemen in frock coats and striped trousers. Kimono-clad women, carrying babies papoose-fashion, waited patiently in line at the numerous cinemas. I saw young boys in white shorts and polo shirts dragging a portable shrine through the streets, followed by a clutch of clamorous children in striped *yukatas* and white headbands scrawled with red hieroglyphics. That same day I witnessed a more fanatical procession — students demonstrating against H-bomb tests, snaking through traffic, shouting and carrying placards. One of these read, "I don't want to eat contaminated fish!"

Across the Plaza, just two blocks from the Tokyo Station, the Imperial Palace rose majestically above a terrace of turfed grass and gnarled pines. It was walled off from the public highway and surrounded by a sixteenth-century moat, where stately swans glided among water lilies, dazzling whites against the green grass and willow trees.

Even a blind visitor could tell that the Japanese had one foot in the Orient and the other in the Occident. The roar of elevated trains drowned out the melancholy chant and flute music of the *komuso* — temple priests begging alms in

46

their black *yukatas* and huge basket hats. Pneumatic drills blasted away at three subways in process of construction, clashing with the brass band of the *chindonya* — sandwich-men, who paraded everywhere dressed like clowns.

One day I literally took my life in my hands, cruising around on Kozo's bike. I didn't always remember that traffic moved on the left and so I had some narrow squeaks with *kamikaze*, busses and trolley cars. I marveled at waiters on bicycles. They could balance several trays heaped high with bowls of hot food and not spill a drop. Japanese cyclists are the best in the world. They have to be, what with drivers using horns instead of brakes and pedestrians seemingly blind and deaf. But the most reckless cabby would slow up when they saw an *America-jin* (American human being).

I hit the jackpot in Nipponese courtesy while threading my bike through Tokyo's lanes and alleys — a fascinating kaleidoscope of color and motion. Housewives at bamboo-canopied stalls filled their *furoshiki* (large, gaudy bandannas) with fish, vegetables, fruit, good-luck gods, dress goods and chinaware. The alleys kept getting shorter and narrower. I turned into one that looked absolutely impassable. Boys were playing catch or stalking about on stilts, women were washing clothes, shopkeepers arguing; but when I saw a postman maneuver his bike through these obstacles, I decided I could, too.

It proved a wrong guess. In trying to dodge some jaywalkers, I swerved, lost control and crashed through the paper door of a barroom. There was a fearful hullabaloo. When I apologized in fractured Japanese to the barmaid,

47

her eyes widened. "Ah, *America-jin!*" Giggling and bowing low repeatedly, she said in Japanese, "I humbly beg your pardon, O honorable, august sir!"

I backed out, blinking. Would I ever come to understand these Orientals? What made them shrug off a street accident but take the blame for a stranger's blunder?

VI
G. I. ON THE LOOSE

The next day something happened that broke the placid summer of my trip. I had been browsing around the Asakusa market place in Tokyo, where merchandise was cheap. I paid only fifty cents for a blue and white kimono and a red *obi*. I hoped my mother would like the patriotic combination.

Bang in the center of this vast, raucous bazaar was the Kwannon Temple — a large, gray concrete structure with a greenish tile roof. In the courtyard a *sumo* (wrestler) stood praying for success in a forthcoming match, his white *obi* worn rakishly low on his splashy *yukata*. Although Kwannon is visited mostly for spiritual ills, the diseased and crippled also flocked to the Goddess of Mercy, hoping for a cure. One man, whose face was swathed in bandages, dipped his hand in the large bronze incense jar and touched his injured cheek.

Children romped about the holy place while their mothers clustered around the gray stone lanterns to gossip. It was like a county fair. I joined a circle of spectators gaping at a character in white blouse and blue pantaloons. He was going through grotesque contortions, doing sleight-of-hand tricks and balancing acts. The audience stood spellbound as he hynotized one man, jackknifing the fellow's arm so that it couldn't be straightened out. A sigh of relief went up when the operator finally unfroze the arm. All this exhibitionism was part of salesmanship. After exhausting his audience and himself, he brandished a small manual. It seems he was a walking ad for a course in Japanese boxing.

I was wandering aimlessly through the temple grounds when I spied a tall, rangy G.I. in the distance. Wasn't that my Nisei? I walked over to him, shyly introducing myself. "I was hoping I'd run into you again."

He looked puzzled, shaking hands with me. "Have we met before?" he asked in a light tenor. A lock of black hair fell over one eye, giving him an elfin look.

"No, but I saw you from a cab last Saturday, trying to help that boy who got run over. What happened to him? Did you get in trouble with the cop?"

"Yeh, a real hassle." There was a wry twist to his mouth. "Any guy sticks his neck out in this benighted land gets slapped down. Meddling, the cop called it. But I made sure he took care of the kid. Found his name in his schoolbooks. I'm going to look him up at St. Luke's. I just hope his skull wasn't cracked."

"You know, I just can't figure it out." I slung my camera over my shoulder. "Pedestrians don't seem to care — "

"Oh, these Nips are scared of their own shadows," he said contemptuously. "They wear blinders. They're just

Charlie McCarthys, with about as much zip as that stone lantern."

Was that the answer? I *must* check with Rai. "Is this your first time here?"

"Yeh. I'm on furlough from Korea. Sergeant Tomo Ta-suki." He made a mock bow. "Tom to my pals — if any! Thought I had friends in Tokyo, but I was all wet."

I had heard that Nisei were disliked in Japan because of having served as spies and interpreters for Americans with Nipponese prisoners. When he said he was staying at the Imperial Hotel, I stared. *It* was high-class, but he wasn't. Maybe he was trying to make a splash.

"What are *you* doing in Japan?"

I told him about the AFS, and he said, "Oh yes, I've heard of it. Great setup. I'm a Stanford man myself. Born and raised in Cal, like my parents. They're truck farmers." A shadow crossed his face. "Right now I'm at loose ends. How'd you like a guide?"

"You bet. I'm lost in the shuffle."

"Swell." He grinned like a schoolboy promised a holiday. "Of course, my Japanese isn't so hot. I can't speak it like the Nips. Fact, they don't understand me. But I'll do my best. How about taking a gander at the Ginza?"

On the way to the subway station, people stared at the American serviceman with the Oriental face, girls in par-ticular. In spite of the slanting eyes, high cheekbones and coal-black hair, he looked Yankee. It was a proud, sensitive face, and somehow forlorn.

As we surfaced near a barbershop he said, "Mind if I stop for a haircut?"

"Go ahead. I could use one myself. I'll meet you there. Have to make a call."

I wanted to confirm a tennis date I had made with Pete Martin. I walked into a public booth and found a notice posted in English: "(A) Please ready with 10 coin, take off the transmitter, put in coin and lastly send round the dial. (B) When not connected, put on the transmitter if it was, and the coin will come on the return hole. (C) For the suburbs communication, Please notify it."

Shades of Berlitz, did my Japanese sound like that?

The barbershop we patronized was immaculate, although it was in a squalid neighborhood, streets and alleys littered with pushcarts and sidewalk merchants selling gewgaws and lottery tickets. I was delighted to find that a haircut, shave, massage and shampoo cost only thirty-five cents. For a dollar and twelve cents women could get a "lasting-ever wave" that was said to be superior to any in the States. No wonder I saw so many perms here!

Before we left this *sanpatsu-ya*, the young barber handed each of us a fine linen handkerchief and some pocket matches. "Service," he said with a low bow.

"You can't beat the Japanese for politeness," I remarked, handing Tomo my matches. "I understand some department stores even have cigarette-vending machines that say thank you when you buy a pack."

He shrugged. "Sure, politeness is their stock in trade. *Dozo, arigato* — Please, thank you. For my money, all this salaaming is so much boloney! They'll turn their backs on suffering, but cry their eyes out over sob stuff at the movies or Kabuki."

"Hey, you *are* prejudiced!" I was startled by his violence.

"Prejudiced?" He gave a bitter laugh. "Yeh, I've got a prejudice all right — against hypocrisy and cruelty and injustice, whether it's a Japanese detention camp in the States or an American prisoner camp in Korea." He crushed his cigarette underfoot with an ironical gesture. "Most popular brand in Japan — called Peace." Then, sidestepping the beggars asleep or crouching in an alley, he added, "What price peace! Take a look at those *Lumpen* around here!"

"*Dozo, dozo!*" A filthy, one-armed beggar held out a claw. We gave him some coins. With a ceremonious bow, he darted to a nearby stall and came back devouring two big carrots.

I thought of America with its abundance of food and natural resources. This side of Japan wasn't meant for tourist eyes — hunger, poverty, disease, despair. Beggars were Japan's biggest problem, said Tomo. The war had left hundreds of thousands homeless — human wrecks who slept under bridges, in railway stations, underground tunnels, parks, empty stores — anywhere they could find shelter.

"Forgotten men waiting to die!" he muttered grimly. "Most of 'em are war casualties. You'd think the Government would look after its vets, especially the unemployables. They still wear their tattered uniforms — pretty faded after twelve years. Now don't get me wrong. I have no use for Jap soldiers. Brainwashed robots. But the war's over, and I can't hate a man who's down and out. The Nips just pretend those beggars don't exist."

That jolted me. "Are you sure?" It didn't gee with what I had seen so far.

"You'll find out. Here the dead are more important than the living."

"What do you mean?"

"Have you been to Nikko, Nara, Kyoto? No? Well, when you see those holy places, you'll know what I mean. Billions of yen tied up in swank temples and shrines and castles and palaces. The Government has been taxing people for centuries, bleeding them white, and for what? Mausoleums, relics, shrines. It's the dead robbing the living."

He upset me with his cynicism. I breathed easier when we had passed the Shiba Park Hotel and came to Ginza Street. No sign of poverty here. Everything suggested wealth, elegance, leisure. Smartly groomed women of all nationalities strolled along the wide thoroughfare. Ginza was the Fifth Avenue of Tokyo, with a dash of Broadway thrown in. East and West clashed in a confused welter of sights and sounds — tiny shops and dingy stalls sandwiched between fabulous department stores, neon lights and gigantic balloons trailing streamer ads, loud-speakers pouring out everything from "Bye Bye, Love" to plaintive geisha ballads.

"Shoppers' paradise." Tomo jerked his head at a fashionable *depato*. "Let's see what goes on among the swells." He winked at me as an attractive hostess smiled, bowed and welcomed us with, "*Irasshai!*" Piped music was interspersed with commercial announcements of a sale on Satsuma dinnerware.

I was dazzled by the merchandise. Such a lavish assortment of goods, Oriental and Occidental, I had never seen anywhere. Some of the coral and crystal and silks belonged in museums. In the crowded dress-goods department, where kimono material was draped over *torii*-like racks, I had the embarrassment of bumping into a kimono-clad lady. I begged her pardon before realizing that I had apologized to a wax dummy. Shoppers stifled giggles behind their hands. But I had the feeling they were laughing with me, not at me.

"You can hardly tell the difference," I said with a sheepish grin. "The women are so poised and statuesque."

Tomo grunted. "Yeh, you'd never guess from the way they carry themselves that they're second bananas." He indicated a salesgirl. "They're drilled like Rockettes. If another customer steps on your toes, it's the clerk who must apologize. They'll lick your boots for twenty-two dollars a month. That's all most of 'em get."

From all sides we heard polite refrains, the escalator girl chirping, "Watch your step, enjoy your shopping"; the clerk: "Thank you for honoring our store with your presence"; the elevator operator: "Thank you. . ."

Tomo followed me into the elevator. "Wait'll you see what's on the roof!"

What I saw was a regular carnival — a zoo, museum, even a Ferris wheel. Children were having a wonderful time.

"You get the psychology," he said dryly. "When Mamasan knows her kids are safe and happy, she's more apt to make a whole day of shopping and spend that much more dough. These stores are open Sundays but closed Mondays. You know, they even hold weddings in here!"

I followed him out in the street, riled by his attitude. Why did he have such a chip on his shoulder? It rankled to hear him calling the Japanese Nips and Japs. I'm rather intolerant of intolerance. "I have to be getting along," I said coldly. "My family expects me for dinner."

His face fell. "Aw come on, let's have a quickie somewhere."

"Sorry, bars are out of bounds for me."

"Then I'll settle for a coffee shop."

"All right, but let's have one thing understood, Tomo. If we're going to be friends, you'll have to — When you use words like Nips and Japs, you start a prejudice in me against you."

"Okay, okay." He made an impatient gesture, as we started for a nearby *Kohi-shopu*.

Students flock to these musical coffee shops to hear their favorite composer over a cup of tea or coffee. For twenty-five cents they could listen to live or canned music, long or short hair. We were greeted by Tchaikowsky's "Pathetique," and a pretty hostess wearing white gloves handling the records. Music-lovers sat motionless and silent, some with eyes closed, others staring dreamily into space.

"Bowl o' Java," Tomo said in English.

The waitress looked blank and so I translated. "Two coffees, please."

"You see?" He shrugged. "They understand me about as well as I do them." When the coffee came, he raised his cup and sang out lustily, "Well, cheers and hallucinations!"

"Sh!" The waitress tiptoed over to us, finger at her lips. "You mustn't talk."

Tomo belligerently set down his cup. "Why? Is this Siberia? Come on, Pete, let's go some place where we won't be muzzled."

He was the limit. "I've really got to run along, Tomo. Give me a rain check — "

"Nuts, let's do a pub crawl. I got time on my hands." And he dragged me to a beer hall, where a less reverential atmosphere prevailed. It was a noisy dive filled with students in uniform, drinking *biru* and whooping it up. Sipping *orenji juisu*, I steered the talk into safe channels — the AFS.

"Wouldn't it be great if all young people could live a while in every country in the world! I'm just beginning to appreciate all that America has to give."

He gave me a pitying look. "You're a nice kid, Pete, well-adjusted and all that. But we live in different worlds. You've had the breaks and you're young and full of illusions. I know Jap — I mean Japanese students who went to the States, starry-eyed, but came back stunned. They saw America as it is, not like the Shangri-La they dreamt it was."

There he goes again! Why must he throw cold water on everything? "Tomo, whose side *are* you on anyway?" I said bluntly. "When you ran down Japan I thought you were one hundred per cent American, but — "

"Got time to listen to a short sketch of my life?" He cocked his head, squinting through a smoke ring. "Well, on my tenth birthday, my mother asked ten of my schoolmates to a party. She went to a helluva lot of trouble sending out hand-painted invitations and all the rest of it. See, I'm an only child. I couldn't wait. Well, when the big day came, how many you think showed?" He held up three fingers. "A European kid, a Negro and another Nisei. And that's how it's been all my life."

So that's why he was bitter and distrustful!

"No better Americans ever lived than my folks. They worked hard, helped their neighbors, obeyed the laws and were model citizens in every way. But to Uncle Sam they were aliens and treated as such. Denied citizenship. In 1942, if you remember your history, every single Nisei on the West Coast was put in a detention camp — seventy-two thousand branded as spies and saboteurs for no other reason than that they were of Japanese descent."

His black eyes smoldered. "For nearly two years we were herded behind barbed wire in a lousy Arkansas swamp. When we got out, we found we had no home left. Our farm had been grabbed by some Americans — just like the Nazis confiscating Jewish property in Germany. And they had ruined it. My parents had to move to another part of California and start all over again." The cigarette trembled in his hand. "My uncle, the only one I ever cared a damn about besides my parents, was killed in Italy fighting for a people who stole our liberty and our property." He scraped back his chair. "Don't talk to me about American democracy. Show me where it exists."

I drained my glass. "You've certainly had it, Tomo."

"*Had* it?" He smiled wanly. "I'm still getting the cold shoulder. American girls treat me like a pariah. How long do we have to go on proving our loyalty? Read the record of Nisei achievement and patriotism. It can't be matched."

I got up, wishing I could help him in some way. "Thanks

for everything, Tomo," I said, holding out my hand. "You've given me a lot to chew over. I'll be seeing you."

"You mean that?" His eyes clung to me. "A guy's gotta have somebody to talk to, you know. Remember the name — Tomo Tasuko. Any time you feel like dinner and another powwow, give me a buzz at the Imperial."

"I'll do that. My time's pretty well taken up, but I'll get in touch with you when I can. So long!"

I walked to the nearest bus stop, his sardonic *"Banzai"* ringing in my ears. My emotions were mixed. What had I let myself in for?

VII
GIRLS AND PEARLS

"We're not really callous, Pete," Rai replied, when I asked him about public indifference to street accidents. "It's the *on*."

"The who?" I stared, and so did Arthur and Pete Martin. We were waiting at the Shoyo Club that Sunday for a batch of Japanese students who were taking off for the States shortly. Rai had asked us to brief them on American customs.

"The *on*." And Rai explained, "The debt we owe others. Every man, woman and child in Japan inherits an *on*. It governs our whole life. From birth to death we're indebted to our ancestors, parents, teachers, employers and the Emperor. A good Japanese tries to discharge that debt by obedience, loyalty and service. A man who commits *hara-kiri* fulfills his obligation to his ancestors, just as the *kamikaze* or suicide squad settled their debt to the Emperor."

"I still don't get it, Rai. What has the *on* to do with common decency?"

"*Ano-ne* — it's like this." He leaned forward, steepling his hands. "If any of those pedestrians had tried to help that injured boy, he would have incurred an obligation that might take him the rest of his life to settle."

So that was it. Tomo had skipped that angle. Or didn't he know?

"Besides, we're taught never to interfere, even in extreme cases. Emergencies like street accidents we leave to the proper officials. We must conform to a rigid code of behavior in this overcrowded land of ours, what with ninety million squeezed into an area no bigger than California. We know precisely how and to what extent to repay obligations, and we try to keep the books balanced."

"That's why there's so much exchanging of gifts, I suppose," said Pete Martin.

"Correct. You can't go anywhere without bringing a present, or coming home with one. That's *shukan*. You Americans are lavish and spontaneously generous, no strings tied to your gifts. With us, it's protocol. It would be impolite for me to refuse a gift, for example, and in return mine must be greater than yours, since you made the first gesture. That deepens the debt on my side. We consider it equally rude if you refuse a favor, but if you're in a hurry to return that favor we feel you want to end the relationship."

Arthur shook his head in mock despair. "My mother always says never return a bowl empty, but this — you go too far!"

Rai shrugged. "*Shikata ga nai!* It can't be helped. The hardest debt to repay is one to a stranger. I know an auto

61

mechanic in Yokohama who lost his month's pay envelope after doing a repair job for an American naval officer's family. He was worried sick about it and told me that if the money hadn't been found he would have killed himself. Because it was traced through that American family he never could repay the debt. They had a lifetime *on* on him. He's still bringing the children presents — clever handmade toys and things."

Whew, what a terrific *on* my foster mother had on me!

The Japanese AFSers had begun to trickle into the clubroom, taking their places at the U-shaped table arrangement. They were dressed up for the occasion, the girls in their finest kimonos. I looked at them, their faces bright with anticipation, their eyes shining. Here was a chance to repay Nipponese hospitality in small part.

Some of them had brought their parents, and among these was the mother of Nobuhide, who would be living in Massachusetts. I had met her before. She had come especially to Nishi-Ogikubo to bring presents for my own mother — exquisite fans and handmade lace gloves, and this quaint note: "These are very poor things, but I wish to present you these. If you will receive my humble desire, I will be very delightful."

Rai called the meeting to order — a session that was to last five hours. When he asked me to give a ten-minute speech, I stood up diffidently before an audience of about forty, but feeling a little more confident than at the first orientation get-together.

"Don't expect American people or homes to be like the

movies," I said in English, carefully spacing my words. "Any resemblance is purely accidental. And don't stand on ceremony. Americans aren't used to bows and formalities. Be natural and outgoing" (as if they could) "and talk about your customs and traditions. Take along your kimono and *obi* and wear them. Your foster family and their friends will want to hear about such details as the *mon*." I had learned that every Japanese wore this family crest on the sleeves of his formal kimono.

"At first you'll feel lost and bewildered, but that strangeness will soon wear off. You'll find that Americans are just as friendly and anxious to please as you are." When I warned them that they would probably gain from ten to fifteen pounds, everybody laughed and looked at Yoshiko. She had come back from Delaware twenty pounds heavier. Poor Yoshi blushed with embarrassment. I wanted to sink through the floor.

She was a quiet, self-possessed girl of twenty, an agnostic like Kozo, although she came from a strict Buddhist family. Occasionally her spontaneous charm broke through her shyness and reserve. "How lucky you are to have such a distinguished foster mother," she often said with much feeling. She admired the women of her country almost to the point of reverence. We saw eye to eye on that. I don't wonder so many G.I.'s married Japanese girls. Without exception they were gentle, unselfish and ultra-feminine.

Yoshi's training was typical. She was still a baby when she was taught to bow, sit quietly on her knees, eat with chopsticks, never to complain but always show the world a cheerful face. As soon as she began school, at age six, she was segregated from boys. The sexes met only in classrooms. Of course now they mingled freely in social life.

I asked Yoshi to help select a Christmas present for my mother, the *Asahi Evening News* having recently paid me for an article I had written. Joyce Stallsmith came along that morning and we inspected cultured pearls at the famous Mikimoto Pearl Shop on the Ginza. Yoshi modeled several pairs of earrings in the mirrored cubicle. I found a pair of beauties, but debated a long time about paying sixteen dollars. It would make quite a hole in my budget.

"But for your mother nothing is too good," Yoshi said, looking up at me with one of her charming smiles. "Think of her pleasure. You know, pearls are the gift of gifts to ladies."

"Well, okay, here goes!" I whipped out my wallet with the nonchalance of a tycoon, and felt slightly weak-kneed pocketing the precious little box. It was the biggest investment of my summer. Rai had advised us not to spend too much for our own families or buy anything our adopted families couldn't afford themselves. I wished I could have bought Mrs. Okajima some, too.

Later that summer I visited the Mikimoto Pearl Farm in Toba. I saw women divers, wearing white as a precaution against sharks, working in and out of icy water for half-hour stretches. The pearls were sorted according to size, color and luster, experts turning out a ton of perfect pearls annually. I learned that a cultured pearl was made by inserting some irritant such as a fragment of mussel shell into the live oysters. This started the layers of pearl nacre around the core. Then for many years the pearl oyster had to be nursed and guarded against storms and other hazards.

Whenever I think of Japanese girls now, I think of cultured pearls. The Japanese regard the *shinju* as the most perfect of all gems. Well, so are their girls. Centuries of careful nurturing and grooming have gone into developing their gentleness, patience, charm and dignity. The core of the pearl, artificial, is the tradition of centuries. To me Harusan, without any of Yoshi's educational or social advantages, had just as much luster.

It was partly to see certain celestial treasures that I visited Nikko the following Thursday with Kozo. He said we could there "view" the Sun Goddess's Mirror, the Gem and the Spear. The Japanese like to believe that their beloved Emperor is a *kami*, or god. According to the legend, Jimmu-tenno, founder of the Imperial Dynasty, had brought these miraculous objects from heaven twenty-six hundred years ago, when he descended to earth via the Heavenly Bridge (Amano-hashidate). The bridge fell into the Sea of Japan and became a peninsula. It's a famous tourist spot, of course. If you looked at it upside down, on a day with clouds reflected in the water, you got the illusion of a bridge spanning earth and sky.

After telling me this with tongue in cheek, Kozo explained that the low dais in the alcove of honor (a typical feature of Japanese houses) was where the Emperor would sleep in case he should condescend to make an overnight visit. Naturally the Son of Heaven must always occupy an elevated place.

We started out that morning at five A.M., Kozo having

been excused from school. It was a cool, rainy day and the scenery flashed by the train window in a blurry mist, like a Japanese screen. Nikko was ninety miles north of Tokyo. We arrived in a downpour, as though there wasn't enough water here already — lakes, rivers, cascades! After crossing the torrential River Daiya, I saw the sacred bridge, reserved for the Emperor and his emissaries. It was open once a year to the public, at the annual Toshogu Shrine Festival.

Nikko was one of a hundred holy places every devout Japanese hopes to see in his lifetime. Every week school-children flocked to Nikko National Park, a 141,000-acre beauty spot crammed with historical treasures. For twenty miles or so we drove along the river bank lined with three-hundred-year-old cryptomerias and endless rows of stone buddhas. Kozo said each time you count these statues you get a different total. I was content to take his word for it.

The shrine precincts bobbled with black and yellow oil-skin umbrellas. White-robed, black-hooded Shinto priests held out begging bowls and paddled through the crowds and the rain. I saw tourists from all over the world. When I smiled and said hello to a group of elderly American school-teachers, Kozo asked if I knew them. I shook my head and he looked nonplussed. Then why had I said *haro?* I shrugged. "Just an old American custom!"

The Toshogu Shrine included about a dozen sacred buildings, the most awe-inspiring being the Yomeimon (Sunlight) Gate. My eyes popped at this enormous jewel box. "Fantabulous!" The Japanese had a phrase for it — "One will be so charmed with its beauty that one will not notice the sun setting." Guarding the entrance were two

66

ferocious-looking Fu dogs — wood carvings painted scarlet and overlaid with gold leaf. My enthusiastic guide, Kozo, told me that when this edifice was built, workmen were afraid of arousing the anger of the gods, who alone can create perfection. So the artisans carved the design on one column of the architectural gem upside down.

Building the entire shrine took fifteen thousand men and twelve years. The timber alone would have extended some three hundred and fifty miles if laid end to end. The only plain white structure in the large courtyard was the sacred stable, and there on the façade I saw the wood carving of the three world-famous monkeys, See-, say-, hear-no-evil. Inside we found visitors feeding a fat pony soybeans. The animal was kept alive so that Ieyasu, the great warrior and founder of the Tokugawa Shogunate, could ride it if he should ever return to earth. Another nice bit of Nipponese whimsy!

I thought of Tomo's remark, "the dead robbing the living," when I read in my guidebook that six acres of gold leaf gleamed from the magnificent tombs of the shoguns, or feudal rulers. What a contrast between all this ostentatious splendor and Japanese poverty or the simplicity of Japanese homes!

I snapped pictures while Kozo held the umbrella over my Kodak Signet 40. Without knowing what kind of film I had inside, he tried to adjust the lens. I objected and he said airily, "Okay, okay, I got instinct!" Whenever I charged impetuously across some holy spot, he yanked me back with a peremptory, "No one walk there!" If I aimed my camera at a sacred object, he obstructed my view and barked,

"*Dame, dame!*" This agnostic was a bundle of contradictions. I grumbled, "Everything in Japan seems to be sacred." What wasn't? Tomo would probably have answered, "The human race."

After a delicious lunch, costing seventy-five cents, at the Palace Hotel (once the residence of an Emperor), we hopped a bus taking us to Lake Chuzenji. For eleven miles we jounced over a steep, zigzagging road with twenty-eight hairpin turns, up and up to the dizzy height of four thousand feet. My ears were crackling. We got out to breathe the deliciously cool mountain air and admire the view — rain-drenched, slate-colored mountains in the distance, toy villages hugging the slopes and valleys, fragrant firs looking like church spires, and flaming azalea bushes everywhere.

For an hour we rowed around the oval Alpine lake in the pouring rain. Chuzenji emptied into Kegon Waterfalls, which cascaded down a lava cliff some three hundred feet. After being plummeted below in an elevator, we stood just about a yard from Kegon's base without seeing a darn thing.

I totted up the day's various types of locomotion — subway, train, streetcar, rowboat, elevator, and my size ten and one-half feet. What I had seen was so enthralling that I forgot all about my prime objective until we were homeward bound. Then Kozo produced the joker. He said that those three celestial objects were heavily guarded in the innermost sanctum sanctorum. Hm. Who was kidding who?

VIII
DEMOKRASHI

One night I was writing letters when Kozo burst into my room flourishing the *Asahi Evening News*. "Read here," he said, pointing to the column, "Brush Up Your English." Under the subhead, "English As It Should Be," was this item:

"A G.I. who refused to have a haircut because, he said, he didn't want to look like a 'shaved jackass' — jackass is the name of a bird — was convicted of refusing to obey an order and received a sentence of four months' hard labor."

I hoped it wasn't Tomo, though it sounded like him. I let out a hoot. "Somebody's slipped. A jackass is an animal, a mule."

"*So desu-ka?*" Kozo said absently, and with a glint in his eye he pointed to his unruly thatch, which I kept twitting him about. "I get shave in head, *ne?*"

The phone rang, and he rushed downstairs, shaking the whole house. When I heard his staccato, "Peetah, for you," I dropped my pad and ran down to the corridor, wondering who could be calling me so late. It was Tomo.

"Any chance of seeing you tomorrow? I've got news, great news." His voice spiraled up. "Can you make it, Pete?"

"I'm afraid I'll be tied up during the day. We're visiting schools — "

"Then how about having dinner with me?"

"Well, yes I'd like to, thanks." I kept my voice low. Everything could be heard in these bamboo and paper houses.

"Swell. Meet me around seven-thirty at the Imperial. So long!"

How had he got my address? And what had he to tell me?

I started out early next morning to meet Rai and Pete Martin in Tokyo. Kozo had already left for school. He got up at six A.M., Saturdays included, commuting by train to Keio. That was more than an hour's ride, involving three changes. In the interurban I had another invitation — from a young man in spectacles. "*Gomen kudasai* — " After apologizing fully three minutes, he asked if I would honor him by having dinner at his home. "I am study Engrish and wish to progress in my speeching."

The light went out of his eyes when I said regretfully that my time was limited. He bowed, trying to conceal his disappointment. I felt badly. But if I'd said yes to every offer I'd had from strangers there would have been no time for anything else. Rai was right in saying that the Japanese are desperately anxious to learn English. They're incurable bookworms. You see people reading everywhere — on park benches, in coffee shops, in queues before theaters, in subways and trains.

70

On the bus to the Ikebukuro Elementary School, I told Rai and Pete about that stranger. Rai nodded. "Our young people will do anything to get an education. Japan has one of the highest literacy rates in the world, with 99.7 per cent enrollment in schools. You know English is compulsory."

"Well, it should be a snap after wrestling with Japanese," I said. "Foreigners call your language an invention of the devil, don't they?"

"It's no cinch." Rai grinned. "Our ideographs are really a kind of shorthand. I'll show you." On a small pad he wrote the symbols for man (男) and woman (女). "Each character represents a sound. Instead of an alphabet, we have to learn two sets of fifty Japanese ideographs, besides thousands of Chinese characters. Sixth-graders are supposed to have mastered two thousand, and every university applicant must know at least four thousand."

I whistled. "School kids must spend half their time learning Japanese."

"They do. And speaking it is much easier than writing it. Offhand I'd say writing Japanese with a brush is about five times as hard as writing English with a pen. Some characters have twenty different strokes and each stroke must be exact. Writing "Honorable Grandparent" properly takes several days' work. Calligraphy is a fine art, only one step removed from drawing. That's why the average Japanese child is something of an artist."

I had seen so many children sketching in parks, at shrines and temples and on the beaches. Fuji-san was one of their first subjects. Every child was taught to become as pure and noble as Fujiyama.

"Nine years of school is compulsory," Rai was saying as we came in sight of the Ikebukuro School, a large, gray concrete building. "Six in primary grades and three in lower secondary, which corresponds to your junior high. Then there's middle school, also a three-year stretch, and college — for the lucky ones!"

The classroom we visited contained about thirty-five pupils. Girls, in pageboy bobs, wearing white middies and blue skirts, sat on one side; boys in white shirts and blue shorts on the other. One pupil wore a mask — evidently he had a cold. There was no giggling or fidgeting. They were all quiet as mice, and I'm sure they got straight A's in deportment. Their teacher (*sensei*, a term of reverence) didn't have to rap any knuckles. Every eye followed her pointer at the blackboard, where she demonstrated a geography lesson. Their knowledge of America put me to shame. They could write an essay on Abraham Lincoln or Thomas Edison on order. They knew far more about our country than we did about theirs.

Afterwards in the gym Peter Martin and I told some seventy-five sixth-graders about American schools, Rai interpreting. For over an hour they stood patiently, erect as soldiers, their shoe-button eyes sparkling with interest. They listened, took notes, and asked intelligent questions, mostly about our "demokrashi." A twelve-year-old sage, after getting our opinion of H-bomb tests, said gravely in Japanese, "I agree that atomic energy should be used for constructive purposes only."

Japanese children are truly concerned about peace. After all, they had ringside seats in the last war. Street urchins would look up in the rain and say starkly, "Strontium 90," probably the only English words they knew.

Like every visitor, I fell in love with the children of Japan. They're irresistible — models of good behavior. It was a pleasure to watch them at play or trooping to school, satchels strapped to their backs — red for girls, blue for boys. They were always happy, always smiling. Often they would follow me, piping in shrill treble, *"Haro, desu America-jin!"*

So it was at Ikebukuru. About fifteen of the bravest boys trailed us outside, asking shyly for our addresses. I think they were budding philatelists. The instant we obliged, two dozen more swooped down like a flock of starlings, fighting for those slips of paper. They all wanted American pen pals.

Every night the newspapers carry pleas: "Wanted: An American pen friend." I had several Japanese correspondents already. The day I arrived, I found a letter from Mitsuko, a girl living in Nara. She promised to show me her beautiful city. She had read about us AFSers and chose me, for some reason or other.

"Do you felt cheerful at there? Please informing me by the letter when you will come to here — with who you will come here? I could understand your second letter soon . . . I am in the pink of health every day, but I have had the fever and ill in bed for two days when we held the marathon race. You must not overwork yourself, and I hope you are always fine . . . I introduced my two Phillipines pen friends you already . . . Please don't doubt or forget my friendship. I always mind about you." Signing off, she invariably wrote, "Now I put my pen here. Sayonara for now."

Pen pals enjoyed a great vogue among high school students, and Kozo's school, Keio, was next on our agenda that morning. We had dropped Pete Martin at the railway station — he had another engagement — and on the train I remarked to Rai that middle school here must be really rugged. "Kozo spends at least three hours doing homework. His light is always on long after I've gone to bed."

Rai shrugged. "Nothing unusual about that. Anyone who thinks American schools are a grind ought to enroll in one of ours. Classes last two or three hours. Our scholastic standards are so stiff that higher education is just a dream for most teen-agers. Even bright students have to take college exams two or three times before passing. The competition is terrific. Most jobs require competitive exams, you know. And because of the overcrowded conditions the Government allows only ten per cent of middle-school graduates to apply for college and university."

Then he startled me by saying that suicides were not uncommon among students. "If they flunk, they go to prep school, and they keep trying until the eighth failure. Kozo's lucky. He's bright and his future is all mapped out. He'll be going into the banking business."

The twenty-seven hundred students at Keio, a massive, concrete school building flanked by a large playground, were called the Ginza Boys because they were chiefly sons of wealthy families. Most of them were train commuters like Kozo. I saw no swank cars on the campus, however, just one old jalopy clanking along. Since all students wear uniforms (entitling them to reduced fares and entertainment), a stranger can't tell rich from poor. But an AFS returnee pointed out certain distinctive marks.

"High-school seniors wear black and white uniforms, and their school lives are said to be gray. Those with cheerful faces and in shiny black, neat, but rather baggy, newly made suits are the first-grade students of senior high. The shabbiest, most diligent and serious ones are the seniors. Their caps are often used for shining shoes. Those terrible university entrance exams make the students look pale because late at night is the best time to study at home."

In the first classroom we visited I noticed a whole sea of pale faces among the fifty boys who burnt the midnight oil. Some of them looked tubercular. Slugging away in deadly earnestness, they had no time or inclination for horseplay. Blackboard jungle was an impossibility. Their respect for *sensei* was second only to that for the Emperor.

I was "teacher" at three hour-long English conversation classes, reading to them from an English grammar. They kept asking me to slow down so they could understand. Later Rai acted as translator in the question and answer period. They were delighted by the similarity of our hobbies and interests — jazz, baseball, movies. Their enthusiasm for our "demokrashi" was impressive. They're one hundred per cent for American culture, whether that's Hemingway, *Porgy and Bess*, or bingo. To them America is the most important nation in the world. They regard us as their neighbors, which we are. After all, only the Pacific separates us.

They filed out sedately when Teacher (a woman) said, "The crass is now adjourned to pray bassebaw in honor of

75

Mistah Beru." Then — whoosh — they made a beeline for the playground. Off the leash, they were as boisterous as any Americans. Of course, this was next to the last day of school. The rowdiest of them was the most bashful boy in class. He made me speculate about Japanese restraint. As Rai had said, "Take off our strait jackets and we're as natural as you are."

They made me *ichi ban* at the bat, later insisting I play first base. Their attitude toward athletics is far more serious than ours. All the Keio boys kept clubs, weights and medicine balls at home. They love to discipline themselves and will put in hours warming up for their pet sport. Rai was even more physique-conscious than Kozo, always doing chin-ups and calisthenics for "the body beautiful."

No wonder the Japanese are so skillful! They even outshine us in our own national sport. Everybody goes in for baseball. Next to setting off fireworks, it's their favorite pastime. They play whenever and wherever they get a chance — during school recess, on the beach, in narrow alleys and even hallways. You hear small fry screech, "*Homurunu*," and I've even seen them playing baseball with babies strapped to their backs.

"Those Keio boys certainly have a yen for freedom," I remarked on the train. "Excuse the pun. I can see why Japan fits in so well with the AFS program."

"Yes, but they're hopelessly confused," Rai answered. "They mistake gadgets for goals and license for liberty."

"You mean like Kozo thinking he's being democratic when he smokes and plays *pachinko?* Oh well, he'll outgrow that."

Tokyo Station was just a short walk to the Imperial Hotel. I had an hour to kill, so I dropped into a movie — admission fifty cents. Japanese cinemas are more expensive than the Kabuki Theater. The people are crazy about American films, and now that kisses and emotional close-ups are no longer censored the audience can let down their hair without losing face, as it were.

I caught the tail end of *Gunfight at the O.K. Corral*, with Burt Lancaster and Kirk Douglas. On my way out, I saw sweethearts (*koibito*) entwined in Romance Seats, which cost thirty cents more. Needless to say, that last row without armrests is never empty.

Neither was the Imperial, although it had about as much distinction as a slag pile. "A great big ugly brown toad," one observer described it. The crowded lobby echoed with a babel of foreign tongues — French, German, Spanish, Chinese. I saw saris and turbans, Scottish kilts and Australian swagger sticks. Then Tomo came out of the bar, flicking ashes off his uniform.

"Hi, Pete!" His face lit up like a Christmas tree, and I winced at his handshake. "Great seeing you again! How about a good, thick, juicy steak?"

"Well, if it's all the same to you I'd prefer Japanese food and atmosphere." I asked him how he knew my address.

"The newspapers." He grinned. "You can't pick up a rag in this town without seeing American AFSers spread all over the pages."

"Well, I'll be darned! I never thought of that." Of course. That was how Mitsuko had reached me.

A woman beggar huddled in front of the restaurant. Instead of tossing her a coin, Tomo held the door open for her, whispering, "Watch this." She walked in timidly. When the outraged proprietor threw her some money and shooed her out, Tomo gave me an eloquent look.

"You remember the kid that got run over?" he said with suppressed excitement, as soon as we were seated in a small, private room. "Yutaka Tashagi's his name. Well, I made a buddy of him. Went to see him at St. Luke's. Doctors said he had a mild concussion and a busted arm. He's out now. Cute kid." Tomo's face softened. "So darned polite he tried to sit up on his *futon*, splints and all, and bow when I brought him a paper airplane. Imagine!"

After the waitress brought the makings for *sukiyaki*, I said casually, "I found out why the Japanese walk away from street accidents, Tomo. You said it was because they wore blinders. Well, it's all explained by the *on*. Didn't you know?"

"Sure I know, but that's just eyewash." He smiled derisively. "Don't kid yourself, Pete. These people — " He broke off as the waitress came to cook the *sukiyaki* on the table grill. When she had served us and left, Tomo said in a low voice, "They're compulsive and cruel because they have a whopping inferiority complex."

"It's *not* cruelty." I gave him a stony stare. "It may be that they've become so hardened to suffering that — "

"You've been here how long? Not even two weeks? I'm Japanese by birth. Don't you think I know what makes them tick?"

Silenced but not convinced, I picked up my chopsticks.

"They're riddled with taboos and rituals. Way behind the times. Girls truckling and kowtowing to their menfolks. But sometimes you run across somebody — " He leaned forward, his black eyes snapping. "Guess where I was yesterday. Having tea with Yutaka's family in Shonan in a seaside villa garden, with servants bowing all around me. His mother wrote me a formal note. She's very refined. They're high-class Japs — Japanese — and strict Buddhists." He sopped up the gravy on his plate with rice. "When his sister walked in, you could have knocked me for a loop. Kiku looked just like her name — chrysanthemum — in that yellow and green kimono." He closed his eyes and sighed. "Golden skin, satin cheeks, and a handle-with-care look about her. The Tashagis couldn't do enough to thank me. I'd like to know people like that," he added wistfully.

I was glad he'd found something to admire in Japan, although they sounded out of his league. "Well, as a Good Samaritan you're in a strong position."

"Pete, you live with a Buddhist family. Think I have a Chinaman's chance?"

"I don't know, Tomo. My foster brother is different from his mother. She's traditional Japanese, he's modern-minded like all teen-agers I've met so far." I started on the iced pastry, light and feathery as snowflakes. "You know, visiting those schools today was an eye opener. Those kids certainly admire America. One boy said please be sure and tell my people that the Japanese are quick to forgive and don't hate or resent us."

"The younger generation is sincere enough, but such talk

from the older ones is just window-dressing." Tomo pushed back a lock of hair impatiently. "They carry grudges and never forget an insult."

"Neither do they forget a kindness."

"All the same, American superiority gets under their skin. And how can they forget what we did to them? You'd think every time they saw a Yank they'd spit in his face."

Now he was taking *their* side. What a weather vane! "What would that get them?"

He shrugged and lit a cigarette. "I'll go along with you to this extent. While the Germans blame their leaders for the war, the Japanese blame only themselves for having been fooled by the military, the samurai, pulling a fast one. They're hated here — and how!"

That jibed with Mrs. Okajima's remark. She said it would have been terrible if the *daimyo*, the war lords, had won the war.

"During the Occupation," said Tomo, "MacArthur got about forty thousand letters a month from Japanese Christians, I understand. Some of them were written in blood, and they all repented their 'crimes against civilization' and blessed him for delivering them from militarism."

"My foster mother told me that her people were far more impressed by MacArthur riding in an elevator with a common Japanese carpenter than they were by the total power of the U.S. Army. You think Japan will ever have true democracy?"

"Nix. There aren't any Thomas Jeffersons around here." He rose. "I'll find out just how democratic they are. I don't think Kiku's a snob, and if her parents are willing to have her date a Nisei I'll take back all I said about hypocrisy."

Maybe their hospitality would make him feel less bitter and lonely. As we parted that evening, I wished him happy hunting.

IX
HEARTBREAK

"Eureka, we made it!" I fell, panting, in the coach seat beside Kozo and facing Tonchi, Tamie and Kouno, his schoolmates. Loaded down with knapsacks, canned food, tennis rackets, cameras, we had battled our way through the crowds at Ueno Station to get places on the early morning train to central Honshu.

Tokyo was an oven I was glad to escape. A pleasant prospect, spending a week camping in Tonchi's hut in the mountains of Karuizawa!

The train was packed as always, but there were no elderly women among the standees, thank heaven! As we pulled out, the stationmaster touched his red and gold cap in a smart salute to the engineer, box-lunch venders shouted, "*O-bento, O-bento*," and passengers settled down, most of them, to reading. One woman nursed her child (he must have been all of four), while several men sat cross-legged and stripped to their underwear, fanning themselves. The floor was littered with *geta* and teapots.

"Tickets prease thank you master tickets prease thank

you master . . ." The conductor's nasal monotone was as irritating as his jerky bows.

Kozo's chums were a friendly, lighthearted bunch. They made a game of speaking English. "You practice archery?" asked Tonchi, the tallest and most levelheaded. He spoke English quite well, his mother having lived in Great Britain.

I grinned, shaking my head. "That's strictly for the birds."

Four pairs of black, slanting eyes regarded me vacantly. Then the good-looking Tamie asked, "You pray feetsbaw?" It was my turn to look blank. He let go with his foot. "*Ano-ne* — keek, keek — "

"Oh, football. No, my game's tennis. And basketball."

"I ride scootah," said Kouno, a funny card. He was quite a tease, refusing to let me see what was in the box he kept in his lap.

It wasn't long before his "honorable inside become empty." We opened our box lunches. The cold rice, fish, pickles, lotus root and radishes were about as filling or appetizing as the chopsticks I found inside.

Passengers had thinned out considerably when we heard the wheeze of an accordion. I looked around and saw a leg-less *heitai* — a war cripple — stumping up the aisle. In the sudden silence I sensed every one recalling the horrors of war. I felt eyes boring into my back as I dropped a coin in his cup. Back home our minister once said that the real test of an inferiority complex was to try and look a beggar in the eye. I couldn't.

"Japanese sight is berry beautiful," Kozo was saying proudly.

Beautiful and varied. There were waterfalls, gently rolling hills, deep ravines, mountains dipping into lakes, thatched houses clustered in valleys. Farmers guided ox plows; fields were strewn with straw and bamboo scarecrows; women in white kerchiefs dotted the rice paddies; tea-pickers wearing peaked straw hats gathered leaves on hillsides, baskets strapped on their backs.

The train shot into a tunnel — one of many — leaving us coughing and gasping. We weren't always fast enough about shutting the window. Along a river bank I saw a typical scene — endless lengths of kimono material drying in the grass. The brilliant colors and stripes blanketed the earth like a vast rainbow. Further on were more strips of blue, pink, green, yellow, being washed in a river to set the dye. Fastened to a raft, they fanned out like ribbons from a Maypole.

At two P.M we arrived in Karuizawa, a popular summer resort three thousand feet above sea level. At the little village of Katsukaki we piled into a truck and bounced over potholes and muddy roads. A half-mile-long footpath led to Tonchi's log cabin. It stood among high grass and tall pines at the base of Mount Asama, this active volcano looming some five thousand feet above us. I had heard horrendous tales of thwarted lovers and frustrated students hurling themselves into its fiery crater.

We dumped our gear on the front porch of the three-room cabin. "Gosh, this is great! Real wilderness — far from the madding crowd!" I filled my lungs with fresh, pine-laden air. At last I had enough space to turn around in. All I could see were rice paddies and trees. Birds sang all around us and there were all kinds of wild flowers — anemones, orchids, tiger lilies. . . A solid week without any social interruptions!

"Beeg snake here," Kouno warned, as we hacked our way through the underbrush on a reconnoitering expedition. "Berry dangerous!"

I saw only mosquitoes and oversized moths. But when we returned, I spied a large green critter hugging a tree. I recoiled. Kouno doubled up with laughter and pulled the realistic-looking paper snake off the branch. So that's what he had in his precious box! Kid stuff! I felt piqued. Kozo slapped his sides at Kouno's antics. "Ho-ho-ho — beeg joke!"

Supper was a simple meal of rice, bread and corned beef hash (eaten out of the can). I had brought a delicacy — canned smoked oysters. The label was equally choice: "Packed in Japan with diligence and responsibility for Safari Foods. Serve cold or not with lemon perhaps. It is assuredly advised that all who delight with their cocktails will happily engage in serving this most sincere brand."

My hopes of a Thoreau-like existence were shattered that evening, when we wound up a two-mile hike at a farmhouse and Tamie whispered, "Girr friendo from Yokohama." It seems I had crowed too soon. "That social call proved fatal for Kozo. He fell hard for a *garu* in a blue sweater. Koharu was visiting her grandmother with a "friendo." He couldn't take his eyes off her, and I didn't blame him. Koharu was a knockout — sultry eyes, a rosebud mouth, and an Italian haircut.

We sat on *tatami* in the best room, the girls waiting on

us like slaves, serving refreshments, fanning us, and chattering in their native tongue. Neither they nor *Obā-san* spoke any English. Altogether it was a sticky evening. But I was interested to see that this household had both a Shinto and a Buddhist altar, or god-shelf, with a name tablet of ancestors. A picture scroll in the *tokonoma* showed an old man holding a bundle of rice. Tonchi said that was Inari, god of the crops. Paper charms over the door lintel warded off disease and catastrophes, such as typhoons, fires and earthquakes.

"We go biking tomorrow, *ne?*" Kozo's pleading eyes were on Koharu.

That favorably settled, he strutted home like a rooster, chinning himself whenever he came to a low stout branch. This seemed to be the season for Cupid. First Tomo, now Kozo! He spent a restless night, muttering and tossing on his *futon*, waking me up periodically. Through the window I saw a star-spangled sky and heard the cuckoo's night song above the harsh rasping of cicadas. They sounded like the train conductor.

The next day dawned cool and overcast. We were up at six. After a hasty breakfast, we began an eight-hour trek on rented bikes, exploring the mountainside. Some of the roads weren't safe to walk on, let alone bike on. Kozo stuck like glue to the Blue Sweater, as we dubbed Koharu. She seemed to like him. All the girls did. He had made a hit with our AFS coeds. His engaging grin and that daredevil streak!

I kept holding up progress, snapping pictures. One was of a woman plowing with a cow — an all-feminine operation. Another shot was of two kimono-clad women with parasols crossing a red-lacquer arched bridge, a couple of fishermen in peaked hats steering a *sampan*, and a mountain in the background dwarfing the thatched-roof cottages along the river bank. It was a Hiroshige come to life, or rather, nature imitating art.

From a distance the rice paddies were giant jigsaw puzzles; at close range, mud puddles. Each row was separated from the next by narrow dikes. Rice needs lots of water. Growing it is backbreaking work. Every shoot, when it's a foot high, is transplanted *by hand* to an even muddier paddy. The water isn't run off until the rice is almost ripe.

The average farmer, according to Tonchi, gets two crops a year if he plants every inch of the soil, and here land is cultivated right up to the roads and beaches. Nothing is ever wasted in this mountainous country, where only fifteen per cent of the soil is arable. The great chain of volcanoes forming the spine of Japan takes up so much space (and so also do the landing strips commandeered by the American Air Forces) that some towns are built dangerously close to live volcanoes.

Peasant women in *mompei*, or baggy coveralls, and straw sandals smiled and waved at us as we rolled by. Japanese farmers are a hardworking lot, up before dawn. Most farms in Honshu are two acres in size. Little or no livestock is raised, as devout Buddhists eat no meat. The poorest keep their money in their mouth. Almost every smile exposes a gold tooth. When Papa-san dies, the farm goes to the eldest son. The younger boys seek their fortune in the city. If they don't make good, they can always return to the farm.

"We go up vorrcano, *ne?*"

Scale Mount Asama with our bikes? I groaned. Was Kozo out of his mind? No, just in love, I decided, as Koharu squealed in fascinated horror. Since I'm an Eagle and Assistant Scoutmaster, I couldn't refuse the dare. I began the ascent with my fellow lunatics, pushing my bike past loose volcanic soil and silently cursing my foster brother. My knees turned to spaghetti long before we got halfway up the road. Oh well, only twenty-five hundred feet more to go!

Tonchi translated the first sign we came to. "Since our researches have led us to the conclusion that the sacred mountain of Asama will shortly erupt again, we would enjoin upon all to reflect earnestly before attempting to climb it."

A second sign said tersely: *Keep Out!* Underneath was a grinning skull and crossbones. I sagged, picturing ourselves buried in hot molten lava. "Hey, don't you believe in signs?" I shouted after them. I could have wrung Kozo's neck.

Four hours of this rugged nonsense and I was bathed in sweat, my throat parched, my head throbbing. I was ready to drop into that live crater from sheer exhaustion. Then we saw a third sign on the summit, this one in English: *Sunset Lookout!* Nothing about danger. The view was breathtaking. To the west were the lofty peaks of the Japan Alps, three volcanic ridges like purple and charcoal theatrical gauze stretching across the wildest part of Central Honshu. "Fantabulous!"

"Fantabulous!" Kozo echoed. "*Suteki!*"

Glorious it was. Due north across the Sea of Japan was Siberia — invisible, of course, but the very thought of it chilling. After getting my mind, I had the heady feeling of a mountaineer surveying the world from a pinnacle. But I was disconcerted to find another party of viewers here. They stood motionless and silent. Worshiping nature is a solemn ceremony, dear to the Japanese.

Fuji now was to the south but, as always, wreathed in mist — like the people themselves. Tonchi said that thousands of pilgrims climbed the sacred mountain in summer — women with children strapped to their backs, men carrying their grandparents. They tread the worn trail wearing white and carrying lanterns, staffs and straw mats that serve as rain-coats and beds, chanting songs about Fuji-san. Adobes of volcanic ash serve as rest-houses along the two-mile ascent.

Was it a dangerous climb? No, Fuji was an inactive vol-cano. Just long. It took from dusk to dawn. " 'If you do not climb Fuji once you are a fool,' " said Tamie, quoting a Jap-anese proverb. " 'But if you climb it twice you are also a fool.' "

We were just half an hour scrambling down Mount Asama. I vowed never again. In fact, I doubt if I could ever repeat that grueling feat.

Koharu's grandmother invited us to supper. It began with a delicious macaroni and duck soup, but I could happily have skipped the raw fish and the *yakinori* (seaweed to you). The ladies sipped tea; the boys *sake*, Peter Bell in-cluded. Kozo monopolized Koharu. Kouno infuriated him by trying to date her. He stalked out of the house with a baleful, *"Baka!" Who* was the damned fool?

Too bad Cupid had to gum up the works! We had been getting along fine and now Kozo crept back in his shell, brooding over the futility of falling in love. I had to admire his courage. He knew that a crush on any girl would be discouraged by his parents. Many teen-agers do take the plunge, feeling that it's better to have loved and lost than never to have loved at all. The traditional Japanese don't go in for all that romantic nonsense, as Tonchi said. Love might come later, but it was no reason for marriage. That was a duty and family obligation. Maybe they had something there.

Kozo probably wouldn't be marrying for another ten years, and then his parents would choose his bride. It was a safe bet that he'd fight that ancient custom like a steer. Although more and more young people were finding mates through teachers, friends and acquaintances, about sixty-five per cent of Japanese matches were still arranged through a *nakōdo*. This go-between rounds up half a dozen candidates, shows the boy's parents photographs and genealogies of the girls, and once the best of the lot has been chosen the two families meet formally for mutual inspection, the young couple exchanging the requisite one hundred words.

"Group dating, blind mating!" I grinned. "Suppose they don't like each other."

Tonchi blew a kiss. "Then it's *haro* and good-by."

Hello and good-by appeared to be the case with Kozo's *koibito*. The following day he saw his sweetheart again. The girls joined us in rowing on Lake Suwa and later roller-skating at a beautiful sports center. He was prickly as cat briar when we got back. Having hiked at least ten miles and over the worst roads imaginable, we ate like wolves, but he kept saying, "No rike, no eat." He had no appetite and just sat moping in a corner.

Came the third and crucial day. All five of us saw the Blue Sweater and her friend off at the railway station. Their vacation over, they were returning to Yokohama. Kozo was unconsolable at losing Koharu so soon. All the starch went out of him. To everything we suggested he said "*yie*," but we dragged him to the Kusatsu Hot Springs in the hope that hydrotherapy would cure him.

I still don't understand why we weren't parboiled. The bathmaster urged us to shout, "*Yoi yoisho*" at the top of our lungs, to face the ordeal of immersion in the scalding water. Kozo screamed lustily with the rest, but once out of that inferno he went into a coma, brooding over Koharu. Now that she was gone, life had lost its savor.

On the fourth day I was on K.P., washing the breakfast dishes in icy water and working the rusty old pump. He came in, looking like a thundercloud – if a thundercloud can look sad. "We go home zis afternoon."

I was dumfounded. "But why, Kozo?" I asked, hoping to draw him out. "I thought we'd be here a week."

He leaned against the doorjamb, putting his head in his hands. I kept pressing him until he said in a sepulchral tone, "I have heartbreak."

So we packed our gear, the atmosphere thick with gloom.

On the train back to Tokyo he droned on and on about Koharu, while I amused myself by making up an essay in Orientalized English.

Kozo he mobo. He rike miruku seiki and raisukare and

keki with bata and kohi. He wear surippa, waishatsu and oba with hankechi peep out. But he know about moto and pomp too. He not care for haikara. His friend is moza. She wear seta and has prety itto. Her apato is in big biru. She make omoreto, boiro ekisu and kuroketo. She also chew supiro gomu. She for Hariwuddo, so Kozo take her to toki. They go skeito, dansu and haikingu. But now rubbry radie fly away, so Kozo have heartbreak.

Translation: Kozo is a modern boy. He likes milk shakes and rice curry and cake with butter and coffee. He wears slippers, white shirts and an overcoat with a handkerchief peeping out. But he knows about motors and pumps, too. He doesn't care for high-collar (people who put on airs). His friend is a modern girl. She wears a sweater and has lots of *it* (sex appeal). Her apartment is in a large building. She makes omelets, boiled eggs and croquettes. She also chews spearmint gum. She's for Hollywood, so Kozo takes her to a talkie. They go skating, dancing and hiking. But now the lovely lady has flown away, so Kozo has heartbreak.

Underneath all that gruffness and truculence he was really a lovable guy. He could be as thoughtful as his mother, checking my bags to make sure I had packed everything. The sneakers I had forgotten to pack for this trip I found neatly wrapped in newspaper. Little things like that endeared him to me. He gave me a great deal of his time, taking me sightseeing and buying souvenirs and gimcracks for my brothers and sisters. We're both philatelists, and I know he'd love to see my collection of four thousand stamps. I wished I could take him back to Gloucester. What fun we'd have!

X

FESTIVALS AND
FIREWORKS

That evening as we approached the house I heard that romantic bell-ringer again and asked Kozo what it was. He brought me down to earth with a thud by telling me it was the night-soil collector.

As soon as he rang the doorbell we heard the patter of feet, then a pause while Haru-san put on her *geta*. "*Konban-wa!*" We said "Good evening" simultaneously. She beamed, curtsied, helped me off with my raincoat and insisted on carrying my luggage upstairs.

Mrs. Okajima was as glad to see me as I was to see her. I had missed her gentle voice. I had missed all the familiar sounds in the neighborhood — the clatter of *geta*, the smack of baseballs striking mitts, children's laughter, the plop of the newsboy's morning paper in the mailbox, the ringing of bicycle bells, the weird music of the sandwich-men and the singing of a night stroller happy with *sake*.

It was a nice neighborhood, not noisy as a rule, except for children playing in the street. Our neighbor's youngsters were full of fun but always considerate of others. The previous week I had noticed in their garden two bamboo poles decorated with colored streamers and slips of paper. I asked Mrs. Okajima about them.

"Ah, *Tanabata Matsuri*," she said softly, smiling. "*Ano-ne* — prease excuse — " and, fetching her dictionary, she translated, "Seventh Evening Festival," then explained that girls who wish to become skilled dressmakers wrote poems and prayers to Vega, the Weaver Star, on July 7. They had to use a special colored ink, mixed with morning dew taken from rice plants or from the leaves of the yam.

It was a charming legend of Chinese origin. Altair, the Herdboy Star, and Vega were lovers. Vega provoked the anger of her father, the Heavenly Ruler (Pole Star) by neglecting her loom for the pleasures of love. So they were both punished with separation. However, they were allowed to meet on the seventh day of the seventh moon on the shores of the Heavenly River (the Milky Way), provided it didn't rain. A large flock of magpies appeared, forming a bridge for them to cross.

The Star Festival was the most romantic of all *matsuri*. Each month there was at least one festival. Everything seemed an excuse for celebration — dragonflies and butterflies unintentionally killed during the year, broken sewing needles, the end of the rainy season (*tsuyu*), cherry blossoms . . . Boys' Festival came on May 5, when all boys were automatically a year older, regardless of their birth dates. For every son in the family the household flew a

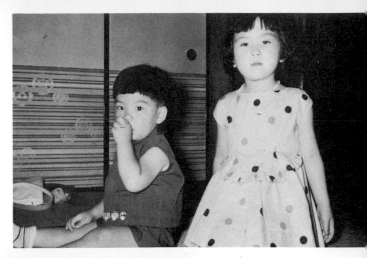

The Rising
Generation

Kids and Dolls

windsock or kite from a bamboo pole — realistic-looking re-
productions of the carp. This fish symbolized courage and
stamina.

Mrs. Okajima tried to get that across to me the day she
took me to a "small creature" zoo at Inokashira Park. I had
no idea where we were going, although she kept imitating
birds and animals, twittering, and making duck-bill motions
with her fingers. After feeding the speckled and scarlet
carp in the pond, she vibrated one hand and brought the
other swiftly upwards — the carp fighting its way upstream
against rapid currents.

I never saw her so happy as when her two older sons and
their families arrived on July 14 for the ancestor-worship
ceremony, which launched the three-day *O-Bon* Festival.
Far from being a joke, the mother-in-law is a greatly re-
spected (and feared) figure in Japan. Mrs. Okajima's daugh-
ters-in-law obviously adored her. Kozo's eldest brother,
Yoichi, had a girl and a boy, a pair of animated dolls, and
five-year-old Hiroko became my *koibito*. A comic val-
entine, bright as a button and enchanting in her little red
kimono and pink hairbow, she would wake me up mornings
with her unintelligible prattle, and follow me around the
house showing me the clever folded paper cranes she had
made in school, or her pet cricket, chirping in its straw cage.

"It sings her to sleep," her mother said softly. A beauty,
this young mother was wonderfully wise in raising her children. But then, Japanese tots never cry, and they're seldom,
if ever, scolded or spanked.

Kozo's second brother, Yashurohiro, lived in Osaka and
was the proud father of a three-week-old baby girl. I had

forgotten how tiny newborn babies were. He was so excited about their first child that he actually waited on his wife. He was probably too young to know better. I never did get used to the sight of that infant being nursed at table. Except for those feedings, it remained strapped to the mother's back. The two were inseparable. My foster mother said that in another week the baby would be blessed at a Buddhist temple, then formally introduced to relatives and friends and given presents of rice cakes, tiny drums, bamboo flutes and good-luck dogs made of papier-mâché.

It was during the family reunion that I saw the Western Room, designed mostly for entertaining foreigners. I had often wondered what lay behind that door. There was no family skeleton, but I couldn't help gasping at the furniture — two upholstered chairs, an ornate coffee table, a heavy walnut sofa — all shrouded in dust-sheets. The only Japanese object was a Kabuki doll, made by Mrs. Okajima. Even the Oriental rug seemed out of place.

The Western Room corresponds to our New England parlor in a way, and I should have felt at home here among Occidental furniture. But I had already become such an Oriental that sitting cross-legged, sleeping on a *futon*, using chopsticks and wearing a kimono was second nature. I had even come to think of money in terms of yen. (Thirty yen was a real saving.)

That Sunday I witnessed a bizarre ceremony in the den — six Okajimas paying homage to their ancestors. They knelt before the *butsudan*, a black-and-gold altar where pictures of Kozo's grandfather and Buddha were enshrined among chrysanthemums and offerings to the dead — tiny bowls of fruit and choice vegetables. The smell of incense filled the room, the candlelight flickered, and white lanterns overhead cast an eerie glow on the brilliant kimonos of the worshipers.

I knelt in the background, feeling tired and a bit slaphappy. It all struck me as funny, and suddenly to my own horror, I burst out laughing. When Mrs. Okajima turned around, I expected a rebuke. Instead she, too, began to laugh. That set off everyone in the room, even Kozo, who had never looked so solemn. Still the ceremony went on. Prayer beads clicked, Yoichi chanted the *Sutro*, repeating the phrase, "Glory to the Supreme Law of the Lotus," Yashurohiro lit a punk and placed it on the altar, while Kozo kept striking a gong, his head bowed.

What was going through his mind? There seemed to be two Kozos. At home he submitted to all the customs and rituals. Elsewhere he behaved like a typical American boy.

I wondered why his father hadn't turned up for *O-Bon*. Mr. Okajima was due to arrive on Tuesday. Kozo had invited Professor Nishizaki, but our language instructor was in Kyushu, attending the fiftieth anniversary of his great-grandfather's death.

Like our All-Soul's Day, the Feast of Lanterns or *O-Bon* is both a solemn and happy occasion. The Japanese welcome the spirits of their ancestors, who visit their temporal homes either with the help of insects or actually in the form of insects like grasshoppers. (A Buddhist venerates every living thing, down to the tiniest creature. My foster mother one night stopped me from killing a moth, gently coaxing it out of the house with a folded newspaper.) There are family reunions, fireworks, lantern parades and street dancing to flute music and drumbeat.

O-Bon is celebrated at different times of the year, depending on the locale, but all over Japan bonfires are lit — the largest one in Kyoto — so the spirits can find their way. There, later that summer, I saw a magnificent sight. At a given signal, three pine logs were set ablaze on the slope of the Nyoidake Mountain. These logs, two hundred to four hundred feet long, formed the Chinese character *dai* 大 (great).

The next day Mrs. Okajima was so excited that she got her nouns mixed up, exclaiming in English, "My father come tomorrow."

"You mean your husband."

"Hai, hai, my *shujin*. Prease excuse — " She laughed and colored with confusion.

Her elder sons and their families had left, and Haru-san was cleaning the house for the master's homecoming. I pictured him as rather formidable, with Kozo's abrupt manner and speech. I wasn't far off.

On Tuesday morning I was writing letters in my room when I heard a commotion below. I galloped downstairs, full of curiosity, and saw a compact, dignified-looking man of about fifty sitting cross-legged on a *zabuton*, fanning himself.

"Mistah Peetah Beru, I presume?" he said, smiling and bowing. His eyes behind horn-rimmed glasses were as kind as my foster mother's. "You had a good trip?" There was a lilt to his voice.

"Yes, sir." I knelt on a cushion opposite him, feeling shy

and awkward. For all his bluff, hearty manner, he commanded immediate respect. His face was strong and unlined, his black cropped hair peppered with gray. He had an "upper-class belly," something to be proud of in Japan.

"You rike Tokyo?" The fan was suspended.

"Yes, sir, very much."

"*So desu-ka?*" The fan moved rapidly, expressing pleasure. "You pray gorf?"

"Not well. I wouldn't stand a chance against you."

He had a nice chuckle. When he rose, I saw that he was even shorter than Kozo. But he thought big. I wasn't surprised that Kozo used the formal Okajima-san instead of the customary *Otō-san*. Mr. Okajima carried himself with all the dignity of an executive. Before the war the Mitsubishi Shipbuilding and Engineering Company, of which he was managing director, ranked with General Motors. Its trademark, three diamonds, was stamped on everything from electrical appliances to generators.

He had brought home his latest golf prizes, all in the original wrappings so that Mrs. Okajima could have the pleasure of opening them. It was a little game they played. Although these awards were an old story to her, she exclaimed over each and every one — a radio, a clock, silver bowls and cups, T shirts, canned goods, imported foods . . . Kozo gazed enviously at those T shirts. He coveted most of my clothes, especially my white golfing cap with the narrow visor, and was as thrilled as a child with a new toy when my father's "Mighty Mac" jacket arrived from the States.

"It's rike opening Pandora's box!" he said. Trying on the

jacket, he grinned happily. "Now I am best-dressed boy in Tokyo!"

With the master home, I was demoted to second in the Order of the Bath. The whole atmosphere changed subtly; the tempo speeded up. When he clapped his hands, things moved, by gosh! Mrs. Okajima fetched his cigarettes or fan on the double, a devoted Haru-san appeared like magic with his tea. She treated him like a god. I hoped he couldn't read my mind. I was thinking that any American maid would have given him immediate notice.

"Zis afternoon we see *hanabi* with Watanabe-san," he said, beaming.

"Beeg *hanabi* go boom!" Mrs. Okajima outdid Kozo in her descriptions.

"To mark end of rainy season — ho-ho-ho!" Mr. Oka-jima's laughter had a hollow ring. He said he couldn't re-member a wetter July.

I had had to cancel one tennis date after another. We de-spaired of seeing sunshine, and when Old Sol did come out it grew so hot and dusty that we longed for rain again. That wish came all too soon. The air was damp and heavy, food spoiled and everything smelled moldy. You never left the house without an umbrella and boots, and at the first drop from the skies big, black umbrellas went up, covering the streets like a funeral canopy.

That afternoon we started out in two Mitsubishi cars. At Shinkuju we picked up Rai and Pete Martin, both wearing thin, cool-looking *yukatas*. I wished I had worn mine. The sky was overcast, but it was hot and sticky. At Ryogoku we got out of the car, as the streets were barricaded. It was a long walk to the pavilion. Whenever I stopped and waited for Mrs. Okajima, she looked embarrassed and waved me on. Her husband was much amused.

Spectators packed the huge, lantern-festooned pavilion (it had been built especially for the occasion) and overflowed the banks of the Sumida River. At least a million people gathered to enjoy the world's greatest display of pyrotechnics, many more watching over "terebition." Over a million Japanese owned sets.

"Better behave ourselves." Rai winked at Mr. Okajima. "There are about thirty-eight hundred policemen here."

Things were already popping when we shucked our shoes and knelt on *tatami*. Rockets burst into all colors of the rainbow; huge fountains of flame went up from a dozen *sampans*; replicas of Mount Fuji erupted with never a pause between one flash and the next. Necks craned, eyes popped, cameras clicked. The Japanese are terrific shutter-bugs and go in for elaborate camera equipment. I ran out of adjectives and fell back on fantabulous.

It was a highly competitive display, sponsored by leading *hanabi* manufacturers. Leaflets, swirling down from the rockets, advertised the firm in huge Japanese characters. The most spectacular number was an accident. All the fireworks in one craft exploded with a shattering *Boom*, and five men dived into the river.

"That was a real doozy!" I turned to Mr. Okajima, asking him how much it cost to put on a show like this.

"*Sa.*" He scratched his head. "Maybe five million yen."

"Wow! Fourteen thousand dollars going up in smoke!"

We had no chance to stretch our cramped legs, even for

dinner. That came to us, served on trays by charming hostesses. It was the biggest meal I ever ate, or hope to eat. Lobster, fried chicken, ham, roast beef, celery, stuffed eggs, cheese, nine kinds of fancy sandwiches, potato chips, Japanese beer, peaches, bananas, orange juice and cider! Those stuffed eggs — what were they? They had a more delicate flavor than hens' eggs and were about as large as Malaga grapes.

"I never heard of squirrels laying eggs," I said naïvely, after Mr. Okajima insisted they were squirrels' eggs. Was there a twinkle behind those horn-rimmed glasses?

My legs were gradually becoming paralyzed. Mrs. Okajima saw me squirm and urged me to make myself comfortable. That meant sitting cross-legged. I took her advice, but after half an hour of this "informal" posture my spine became numb. I marveled at her own endurance and control. It was a triumph of mind over muscle. When I learned that these pyrotechnics would last twelve hours, my heart sank. Question: Could *I?*

XI
STRADDLING TWO WORLDS

"See you rater, arrigator," Kozo said with an impish grin early next morning.

He was off on a week's golfing trip to Lake Yamanaka. I had overheard him telling his schoolmates on the train that he intended asking Koharu to play golf with him. Strange that he should be going away just as his father had arrived. They seemed congenial enough, although it was hard to say what the Japanese really felt or thought. That smiling mask still had me buffaloed.

I had hoped to become better acquainted with my foster father, but during the day he was away on business, and evenings I generally had some engagement. I would come home just as he was retiring, fan in one hand and a book in the other. The little I did see of him, however, made me want to know him better.

I found out why he divided his time between Osaka and

Nishi-Ogikubo. Mrs. Okajima explained that he had installed his family here so that Kozo could attend Keio, which he considered the best private school in Japan. Sacrifices had to be made for the youngest and last male of the family. I also discovered that her reservations about having an American boy in the household concerned *my* welfare.

"Okajima-san onry one speak Engrish good. He not home much. Boys need father, *ne?*" Then she added proudly, "He come home every month. He strong — mm — famiry man." She looked at me quizzically.

I nodded, complimenting her on her English. It was improving each day. I wished I knew Japanese better. I was missing so much. With her rich imagination, she could have opened up a whole new world to me. She saw everything through the eyes of a poet. Speaking of the rainy season, she said that the *tsuyu* wouldn't end until the topmost blossom of the *tachiaoi* had come out. The lowest flower on this six-foot-high bush was the first to open.

My Japanese coach in Gloucester had raved about the style and beauty of Mrs. Okajima's early letters, and such poems or *haikai* as I was able to translate I found sensitive and charming. In one of them she lamented the rapidly changing world, likening herself to a wilted flower. I knew that Kozo's Western tastes and inclinations disturbed her.

"I will never change," she said sadly, more than once.

She lived up to her name, Nobuko, meaning faith. My own mother and she had much in common. They were both artistic, perceptive, unselfish and extremely conscientious. Everything about Mrs. Okajima symbolized old Japan — her love of beauty, devotion to her family, her delicacy of feeling, and her uncanny, almost telepathic intuition. I loved watching her face. It was so serene. At times her sweetness made me want to cry.

"You feel well, *ne?*" she kept asking anxiously. Whenever I had seen Rai or Yoshi, she would phone them and ask whether I was really happy. There was no end to her thoughtfulness. As soon as she found that I liked milk and bread, she ordered two quarts of homogenized daily and served *pan* at each meal. I thought fruit was *oishi?* Presto, peaches and melons appeared at the table. I liked calves' liver? After that we had it about eight times a week. She would wait for me to come home, even on the hottest nights, before taking her own bath.

On one occasion this was after midnight. I had spent a dramatic evening with Rai, Pete and Ohana, a fragile-looking returnee of twenty-four with a poignant story. She was in delicate health, Rai said, and had had a fainting spell the other day. "That girl's gone through too much."

We had gathered at the Chopin, an elegant coffee shop, each of its six floors catering to a different clientele. The ground floor offered a mixed musical menu, the second one jazz, the third one popular music, and so on. The higher up you went, the more esoteric the fare. We chose the top floor featuring hi-fi classical music, and were ushered up a circular staircase to a dimly lit, cathedral-like chamber with a domed ceiling of stained glass. Shelves along the walls displayed exquisite cut glass and sterling silver.

Rai said that many teen-agers got their musical education at these places. "Long-hair fans go in for Western music, especially German composers, and they'll scrimp and save for months to hear live artists. They talk about 'my Menuhin savings' or 'my Rubinstein savings.' "

We sat listening to Mendelssohn's violin concerto for a while, Ohana with eyes closed, her face like an opal in the subdued light, her hair, brushed back in a large bun, looking sleek as black enamel. She was not misnamed. *Ohana* is the Japanese name for flower. She had been born in China of Japanese parents, converted Christians, but at age eight she and her sister had been taken to Japan by friends of the parents, this married couple having raised the two girls as their own.

"For thirteen years we heard nothing from our parents in Red China." She spoke in a quiet monotone but with great effort. "It was as though they had never existed. Just a week ago we learned their fate. Father had been killed by the Communists and Mother arrested while doing refugee work. Because she had won the love and respect of so many Chinese, she was accused of softening them up for Japanese invasion. She had been in prison three years when the Communists took over." Her voice faltered. "For the next eight years she went through unspeakable torture, in solitary most of the time, living on starvation rations. When the time came for her release, they fattened her up a little. But she was so weak that she couldn't travel for months. Now she's here in a hospital — "

Ohana covered her eyes, tears trickling through her fingers. "I'm longing to see her, and yet I'm afraid — she will be so dreadfully changed — "

There was a strained silence, as we searched for words to express sympathy. My heart went out to her. I thought of the millions uprooted, exiled, cast adrift, rotting in prisons. Rai tactfully switched the conversation to the AFS and his experiences in the States.

"You're lucky," Ohana said with a tremulous smile, after he had described what his year in America had done for him. "I came back feeling restless and dissatisfied. For me it was an unsettling experience. Japan didn't seem real any more. It was like looking through the wrong end of a telescope. I can't adjust to the old ways here. I don't know why, but I feel as though I were half-American."

So many young people seemed to be stranded, groping for something to believe in and hold fast to! Torn between two worlds, like Tomo!

Speaking of my Nisei, I'd seen him the day before in the Marunouchi district, having just left Rai, Arthur and Pete Martin at the Hilltop Hotel, where we were interviewed for a story in *Obunsha*, a girls' magazine. I was heading for Tokyo Station when I saw Tomo hurrying along the Plaza, carrying a big bouquet of roses and box of candy. He reddened and whisked his presents behind his back like a small boy caught stealing jam. "Oh, hi, Pete, I was just — I'm going — Oh hell, what's the use, you know darn well where. She's waiting for me. Have to rush now. Be seeing you!" I grinned and made the V sign. So he was courting Kiku! I feared the worst.

That evening after Kozo and his father went to bed (Kozo had returned from his golfing trip looking like the cat that swallowed the canary, with little to say except that it had rained every day), I sat in the den talking with Mrs. Okajima. She was carving a tray and she made a pretty picture in her jade-green kimono and chartreuse *obi*, her black hair brushed back neatly in soft waves.

"Tomorrow you see my husband's *yadoya* in Kyoto," she said, and making a wide sweep of her arms, she added, "Kiyoto-san live in beeg inn. Many peoperu. We traver second crass."

"How many classes are there?"

"Sree. Men first crass, radies second crass, servant sird crass." She tilted her head. "Prease excuse but radies traver second crass in America?"

"No more so than men. It depends on their pocketbooks. Most of the working people have cars, you know."

"Ah, but you have demokrashi."

I smiled, explaining that husband and wife usually traveled together, whether by car or train.

"*So desu-ka?*" Her eyebrows went up. "Here much different. Radies and men apart." She cut the air with her hand. "In bus or train husband sit, wife stand. No speak each other." She gave a little disparaging laugh, as much as to say, "Isn't it ridiculous!"

"*Dozo — gomen nasai*, Okajima-san." The maid pattered into the den, smiling and curtsying, to ask her mistress something about my red shirt, which she held out.

Between the two of them I was becoming hopelessly spoiled. Haru-san took complete charge of my wardrobe. If my *yukata* got bunched up at the back, she would straighten it. If I knotted my *obi* on the left, she would tie it on the right.

Mrs. Okajima always spoke of her as *jochu* and yet didn't

like us to call Haru-san a servant. Feminine inconsistency! This patient Griselda never thought about herself. A nun couldn't have been more self-effacing. Everything was for others. Each morning she would call my attention to Fuji, saying tenderly, "Honorable Fuji-san hide face zis morning." I spun that out into a little joke. "Fuji hasn't run away yet?"

Unlike most Japanese she was very shy about being photographed. I chased her all over the house one day before she would pose for me. I planned to send her a framed enlargement from the States. My hands were tied by the Japanese *on* and I didn't dare give her a thing, while she kept showering me with favors and little presents, such as handmade dolls for my young sisters, or a make-up kit for Ruby, our maid. It was embarrassing.

Next morning promised to be a broiler. Mrs. Okajima warned that Osaka would be even hotter and dustier. She looked handsome in her navy blue kimono (blue was her favorite color) and brilliant striped *obi*. She seldom wore Western dress. The parasol she always carried while traveling added a charming touch. Our luggage stowed in the green Plymouth, the Mitsubishi chauffeur was just stepping on the accelerator when Haru-san popped through the front gate in great excitement, calling me and holding an imaginary phone receiver to her ear.

I dashed into the house, grabbing the phone. "Hello?"

"Pete?" Tomo sounded frantic, desperate. "Hope I didn't get you out of bed. I'm in a helluva mess. Any chance of seeing you today?"

"Oh Tomo, I'm sorry but we're just trying to catch a train. I'll get in touch with you at the Imperial as soon as we get back from Osaka in about ten days. Okay?"

Click! He had hung up on me. I rushed back to the car, the Okajimas looking at me anxiously. What had gone wrong? I felt like a heel letting him down.

At Tokyo Station Mr. Okajima said genially, "See you in Osaka," and headed for the first-class coach. We settled down in our second-class seats, thankful that the express train was air-conditioned. Kozo dozed during most of the eight hours. Mrs. Okajima had insisted I take the seat by the window. She pointed out bits of scenic interest, interrupting the language lessons we usually swapped when we traveled together.

The train followed the coastal route in a southwesterly direction, winding and twisting like a serpent through the suburbs, the rice paddies, farms with small roadside shrines, groves of golden bamboo and fishing ports. I saw women in white coveralls along the beaches sorting out kelp — war widows eking out meager pensions, Mrs. Okajima told me. My thoughts kept snagging on Tomo. Was he in hot water with Kiku? Well, I'd call him when I got to Osaka.

XII

A JAPANESE GENTLEMAN

A Mitsubishi chauffeur met us at the station and drove us to Asada, on the outskirts of Osaka. Mr. Okajima lived in a big stucco inn surrounded by a high hedge. We walked up a graveled path. In the neat entrance-way, a row of kimono-clad maids (*neesan*) greeted us with broad smiles and low bows, chirping, "*O kyuku san*" (O honorable guests). After surrendering our shoes, we were given carpet slippers, which were to be left at the door to our room.

I felt like a cad letting that tiny *neesan* carry my bag, but Kozo said she would have lost face otherwise. What I dreaded most was the large communal bath. There were no locks or knobs on the sliding doors. Kozo assured me that the ladies wouldn't even notice me.

"How many other guests are here?"

"I sink maybe twelve." And he said, with a gleam of mischief in his eye, "Tonight you come last in bazz. Here Okajima-san *ichi-ban*."

My prestige was waning! The room we shared had the same unfurnished, austere look of all Japanese rooms — a clothes rack, cushions, *hibachi*, and a doll-sized dressing-table. You sat on *tatami* and squinted at yourself in the mirror. I soon saw what a privileged guest my foster father was. The Mikado himself couldn't have had more attention or respect. The maids all but turned themselves inside out to please him. Of course he occupied the best room, at the back of the house and overlooking a lovely garden of miniature pines and stone lanterns. He must have had at least seventy-five golf prizes on display.

We had a seafood dinner that evening, July 29 being Eel Day. I didn't know what I was eating until Mrs. Okajima made serpentine motions, pointing out that eels were rich in Vitamin A.

"We fortify against hot-weather disease." Mr. Okajima smiled and placed both elbows on the porcelain armrests. "I hope you enjoy Osaka. Greatest industrial city in Japan. Some say it is ugly, but there is drama in blast furnaces and shipyards, *ne?*" His black eyes glowed. "Today Osaka largest shipbuilding center in world. You see Mitsubishi plant tomorrow."

Osaka was called the Venice of the Orient because of its countless canals, but it reminded me more of Pittsburgh — smoke belching from a jungle of factory chimneys. Mr. Kinura, a Mitsubishi executive, showed me the one hundred-acre site next morning. In the shipyards I saw American oil tankers being repaired and vessels of all types in process of construction. One, bound for Scandinavia and christened *Oslo*, was to be launched tomorrow. A case of carrying coals to Newcastle!

We drove right through the colossal factories, where

boilers and magnetos were being built. There was no loitering here. Workmen were so absorbed in their tasks that they didn't even look up. Industriousness is the most outstanding trait of the Japanese. People work long hours and every minute counts. And yet several higher-ups took time to sit down with me over refreshments to answer my many questions.

What was happening to the great combines MacArthur had broken up — Mitsubishi and Sumitomo? They were being re-formed. Mitsubishi employed twelve thousand and its latest expansion was the Atomic Power Company. What kind of promotion system did Mitsubishi have? Laborers got pay raises according to seniority rather than merit, and that method applied to all walks of society. What about taxes? They were crushing — even higher than in America. Japan's dilemma, in a nutshell, was as follows: High tariffs offset her main export, cheap labor, and she couldn't afford to buy raw materials. The Western countries were afraid of her competition and she was losing her markets in Asia to Russia and Red China.

I remembered my pen pal, Mitsuko, writing me a garbled bit of information. "Japan is one of the civilized countries, but she has little source of revenue, so she will not be able to conquer the Universe like Soviet or America. It is great pity to us."

The afternoon wound up in Mr. Okajima's office, a large, impressive room dominated by a solid walnut desk. We sat on a sofa before a low coffee table piled high with periodicals (including the *Wall Street Journal*), while a hostess in white served green tea and beautifully iced cakes. But first she brought in those cold damp cloths, *O-shibori*, most welcome in the oppressive heat.

Next morning, the first chance I had, I phoned the Imperial Hotel. When the desk clerk told me that Mr. Tomo Tasuki had checked out, I was really alarmed. What could have happened to him? I left a message. "If you see him, please ask him to phone me at the Okajimas the evening of August 7."

Mr. Okajima took us to a famous *tempura* restaurant that day. After washing our hands and rinsing our mouths at a small artificial spring (Shinto cleanliness), we shed our shoes among an assortment of footgear such as *zōri*, and from a *tatami*-covered level were led into a small room looking out on a canal. The hostess shut the door, for eating is a private affair in Japan. Presently a tiny waitress in kimono brought *ocha*, pouring it out with the grace and composure of a duchess.

When she said politely, "You have lice *and* bled?" I nearly choked on my tea, whereupon the Okajimas looked at me blankly. She kept backing out of the room with deep bows, but there was nothing servile about her. She was so dignified that she made me feel like royalty. The main course, prawns and shrimps dipped in egg batter and fried in sesame oil, went down nicely. *Oishi*. Not so the cubed octopus that followed. Unborn squid may be a delicacy, but no, thank you!

I was getting deeper and deeper in debt to my foster father. He planned my itinerary down to the last detail, sparing no pains, and everything went like clockwork. How many tycoons would have bothered to entertain an obscure American schoolboy? He was a gentleman of the old school, and the soul of tact.

One afternoon Kozo and I practiced putting shots, and I broke one of his father's golf clubs, a three-iron. I felt awful, knowing how much he treasured anything connected with golf. I offered to confess but Kozo said, "No, I go." And he marched up to his father the moment Mr. Okajima got back to the *yadoya*. I trailed along, stammering apologies while Kozo told him of the mishap.

Mr. Okajima chuckled, dismissing the matter with a wave of the hand. "Don't worry. Of no consequence. I have many crubs."

That put him in the front ranks with me. It was a small thing but, like Japanese art, it revealed a great deal. I realized later why he had made all the sight-seeing arrangement behind the scenes. It was to save me the necessity of thanking him. Speaking of the *on*, Kozo made his longest speech of the summer.

"Japanese likes *on*. They think iss important to return *on*. You don't have such kind of system? You think *on* has something to it? Iss not so bad, *ne?* Modern authors criticizing *on*, also young people who doesn't like Japanese — mm — persons who likes things from abroad — Western, anti-Japanese, you know, they think *on* stupid. In my case it iss not so emphasized. Not necessarily to feel *on*."

He often made fun of high-class people, and now he did something unprecedented, stepping out of his station by taking a nice-looking *neesan* to the movies. Capricious as Japa-

nese scenery! What his parents thought of their son hob-
nobbing with a servant I never found out, but I hoped he
was really trying to forget Koharu.

The day before we went to Nara, Dave Brudnoy phoned
me from his foster home in Fukui. Pete Martin was with
him. I suggested they come to Osaka and meet my foster
father. He said he would be delighted to take my American
friends to dinner.

They arrived in time for a powwow, Dave filling me in
on his Japanese home. "My adopted father's full of fun, a
great character. He took me to a wrestling match the other
night. It was held in a village appropriately called Ono."
(An *ono* is an axe or hatchet.) Dave made a comical face.
"It had rained the night before and the whole place was one
big mudhole. We sat mired for three hours. The scene was
a study in contrast — the fanatical way the audience
watched that gruesome contest between a couple of human
oxen trying to push each other out of a circle of stones, and
in the background those beautiful mountains enveloped in
mist — "

"Those wrestlers weigh three hundred pounds or more,"
Pete Martin broke in.

"Biggest men in Japan," Dave drawled. "The only Japanese I've seen who could top my height. Perfectly gargan-
tuan. They eat as much as ten ordinary men. They wear
their hair long in a topknot, and the bone crushers I saw
were tattooed all over with geisha girls, sea shells, tigers and
dragons. Grotesque."

"I'd hate to tangle with a *sumo*."

"Or even with a judo expert," I said with a shudder.

"Remember the matches we saw at the Kodokan in To-kyo?"

The door panel slid back and Mr. Okajima beamed and bowed. "*Konban-wa!*"

"Good evening, sir!" We scrambled to our feet. I in-troduced my friends and was amused to see them as over-whelmed as I had been. But by the time we reached the Chi-nese restaurant Dave was going lickety-split in Japanese. The fabulous eleven-course dinner we had included glazed duck, shark-fin soup and lotus blossoms floating in raw egg. The *sake* was served in dainty porcelain cups with lips that whistled when you drank.

Mr. Okajima chuckled as the hostess bowed us out with a brisk, "*Haro, haro.*" Later he showed us the Shinsaibashi shopping district and the Bunraku-za Theater — the only marionette theater in Japan, and where near life-size pup-pets were operated by three men. I was looking at the post-ers, and turned around to ask him something. He was gone. "Well, I'll be jiggered!"

"How could we lose him so fast?" Pete Martin looked around in consternation.

"There he is — no, that's not him. I just don't understand it." Dave had removed his sunglasses to search the faces streaming by. "We didn't even have a chance to thank him."

"Of course, that's why he slipped away! He didn't want to be thanked. It's that darned *on!*"

I was all the more upset when Dave told me that Mr. Okajima had apologized for being so dull. He was ex-hausted, having just flown in from Tokyo. And tomorrow early he would be flying to Kyushu.

"He said he would be very pleased if all his sons kept up their friendship with you. He thinks you're brilliant, clear-headed, responsive, considerate and very adaptable."

I blushed. "Quite a recommendation, Daviko-chan." The affectionate diminutive, *chan*, made him squirm.

XIII
MY PEN PAL

"There they are!" I spotted the two girls at the Nara railway station, recognizing them by Mitsuko's snapshot. The lovely tall figure in cherry-red kimono or the little schoolgirl in pigtails — which one was my pen pal? She had failed to indicate that.

As Kozo got out of the car and walked up to them, I kept my fingers crossed. He brought them over, slurring the introductions, but I gathered that Mitsuko was the tall beauty with the artificial cherry blossoms in her hair. She looked about ten years older than her little cousin, who came up to my elbow and whose name I didn't quite catch.

Anyhow, she seemed the more outgoing of the two. "How do you do," she said in stilted English, shaking hands. "I am very preased to meet you. This is very happy day for us to show you sights of our beautiful city." She must have sat up all night rehearsing that little speech.

Japanese girls don't go in for cosmetics until they're eighteen, as a rule, and then even the homeliest ones begin to blossom out. We lapsed into self-conscious silence as the

Mitsubishi chauffeur drove us to Nara Park. Kozo, a man of few words, wasn't much help. There he sat, gazing moonstruck at Mitsuko. I tried to start a conversation with her, but all I got was a Mona Lisa smile and a lovely profile turned to the scenery. It puzzled me. If she spoke no English, how could she have written those letters?

"Nara oldest city in Empire," her cousin piped up enthusiastically. "In Naturaw Museum art treasures six hundred year old." She consulted her fat little dictionary. "Nara Park biggest in Japan — has 1760 acres."

She was like Haru-san, so eager to please. "Really?" I smiled down at her, feeling like a sophisticated old uncle. (That's what travel does.)

We stopped to feed the tame deer roaming through the park — fawn with the same soft, melting eyes of Mitsuko. The natural woodlands reminded me of the setting in *The Wizard of Oz* — fantastically shaped trees, crooked, gigantic and witchlike. People moved about sluggishly, fanning themselves. The rainy season had ended at last, and now the most oft-quoted words were, *"Atsui-ne?"* Having moldered throughout July, we were about to be fried to a crisp in August.

I saw few teen-agers but hordes of schoolchildren. Kozo said they saved up their yen each week for annual sightseeing trips like this. Women were picking grass by hand, while beggars squatted before the magnificent temples — temples testifying to charity and brotherly love. Again I thought of Tomo. When I gave an old *Lump* a coin, Kozo scowled. "You never get rid of them." But Mitsuko's cousin smiled her approval.

"I'd like one of those bronze lanterns," I teased, as we admired the Kasuga Shrine, a vermilion structure festooned with bronze lanterns.

She lifted a distressed face. "Ranterns in Nara sacred."

I winked at Kozo. "Oh, but I read that Nara has one thousand bronze and two thousand stone lanterns. Surely *one* wouldn't be missed!"

We followed the ritual of all pilgrims, washing our hands at the purification well, then dropping a coin in the alms box and clapping our hands to announce our arrival to the god within. The schoolgirl bowed her head in prayer, but Mitsuko bought from the priest a spin on the prayer wheel (it looked more like a parking meter). He blessed us with a sacred broom, we burnt incense at the innermost altar, and he then stamped the colored seal of the Kasuga on the first page of an accordion-pleated blank book given me by the lovely Mitsuko.

Apparently we were her guests. I was embarrassed when she showered me with literature, bookmarks, rice paddles, amulets and charms, and tried to express my appreciation by showing her little courtesies. Her cousin, paired off with Kozo, kept giving me bleak smiles. Could she be jealous?

When we reached the gateway to the Todaiji Temple, I asked her about the *Ni-o* or Devil Kings. She floundered in her dictionary with furrowed brow, then gave me a lopsided smile. "I am shorry but my Engrish very poor."

My guidebook told me that these two stone carvings flanking the elaborate entrance were fine examples of twelfth-century sculpture. Dwarfed by the enormous temple, we stood looking up at the world's largest Buddha — a fifty-three-foot bronze Daibutsu cast in 749 and weighing five hundred tons. The right hand (raised as if in blessing) could have held at least fifty people, I'd guess.

"*Beru*," the little schoolgirl announced triumphantly, pointing to the forty-eight-ton bell at the right. "Rike your name."

Obviously it was a bell, but what of its history? She must have read my thoughts for her shoulder drooped. Poor thing – she tried so hard to be helpful! Kozo swung back the heavy beam, grinning with satisfaction as the gong gave off a deep, mellow sound, its vibrations reverberating just as they did twelve hundred years ago. "The sound reaches Paradise," my guidebook assured me.

After conferring with Mitsuko, Kozo said crisply, "We see now oldest temple."

A short drive to the outskirts of Nara brought us to Horyuji Temple. We shed our shoes, adding them to the rows of footgear on the steps of this sixth-century wooden structure, noted for its *objets d'art* as well as its architecture. Nearby was a five-tier wooden pagoda, one hundred and fifteen feet high. The steep, winding rickety stairs we climbed in pitch-dark had not been built for tall visitors. I had to bend almost double, and I was sagging like a rusty old bedspring when I got to the top.

The day wore on and I wore out. The heat was unbearable, stupefying. My feet ached, my shirt was soaked, my throat dry as dust. I came to life as Mitsuko invited us to lunch at a Western-style restaurant. We all ordered steak. Her cousin's reproachful glances continued to mystify me. Why should she feel hurt by my polite attentions to my pen pal and hostess? Or was I off base?

She watched me furtively as we began on the hors d'oeuvres to see what fork I used. When the big, sizzling steak arrived, she shrank in her chair, her eyes downcast, blushing with mortification. "I am shorry but I cannot whole meat eat."

Mitsuko urged her to order something else, but she shook her head, close to tears. I plowed into my steak feeling like a cannibal.

And so went the whole day — a comedy of errors, one frustration after another. We had our palms read by a blind fortuneteller, Kozo translating her prediction that I would receive a letter that would prove a turning point in my life. It sounded ominous. I went all goose-pimply.

We left the girls at the railway station, agreeing to meet tomorrow to "view" Kyoto. Mitsuko smiled and bowed graciously when I thanked her. Her little cousin gave me a sad, stricken look, this time not offering to shake hands. I was baffled.

We started back to Osaka, a two-hour shake-up over terrible roads. I turned to Kozo, lolling in the seat, and said casually, "Nifty number that Mitsuko, but what did you make of her little cousin? She seemed offended. What did I do to upset her?" When he sat bolt upright, looking blank, I said, "Don't tell me you didn't notice. What's her name anyway? I never did catch it."

A diabolic grin spread over his face. "You mix up *garu*. Tall radie Tamami. Short *garu* cousin name Mitsuko."

I let out a squawk that made the chauffeur turn around in alarm. "Holy mackerel! Now I *am* in the soup!" No wonder my little pen pal was hurt! How could I have been so stupid? But then Kozo had mumbled the introductions. The Japanese are very poor at such formalities. Well, I'd try to make it up to her tomorrow.

I told Mrs. Okajima about the day's excursion. She laughed at my mix-up and sympathized when she heard of Mitsuko's defeat by a beefsteak. She herself was indisposed because of having eaten meat, which never agreed with this devout Buddhist.

"Tomorrow you go back centuries into past." Kyoto, she said, was the real Japan, the Classical City where Emperors and shoguns reigned at the height of their glory from the ninth to the nineteenth century. Palaces, castles, shrines, temples — it was a priceless art treasury, and for that reason had been spared bombing attacks. Its geishas were fabulous.

We were up at six next morning. After breakfast, our good-natured chauffeur drove Kozo and me about thirty miles northeast and over good roads for a change. At the Kyoto railway station we found only Mitsuko waiting, with her fat little dictionary. Today *she* wore cherry blossoms in her hair. I braced myself as she stepped into the car. Kozo whispered to her in Japanese and at once her face cleared. She sent me a forgiving smile.

I made amends, asking her about her school life. She responded like a Japanese flower opening in water, although I couldn't understand half of what she said.

"I put Kyoto second on my list of must-see places," I remarked, as we drove past a lotus-fringed lake, which formed a silvery motif against the sloping mountains.

"Oh, you enjoy *takusan* — much beautiful sights here." Her black eyes sparkled. "Kyoto has three thousand holy buildings," she said in Japanese.

I whistled, suggesting that we settle for half a dozen. Our first stop was the Gold Pavilion, close by the triple-tier Kinkakuji Temple. This onetime villa of a court noble was a replica, the original having been destroyed by fire. It stood on the banks of the river, a masterpiece of fourteenth-century architecture, reflections of gold leaf shimmering in the water. Mitsuko pointed to the gold rooster on the roof-tree and giggled politely when I remarked, "You have Kinkakuji and we have Fort Knox."

She tried in vain to translate the inscription on the façade of the Sanju-sangen-do nearby, a three hundred and ninety-six-foot-long hall displaying one thousand and one Kwannons. Her nose was still in that dictionary after Kozo came up with the answer — "The Buddha having infinite abilities for seeing the truth of the whole world." Each of these gold-leaf statues had forty hands and a different expression. When these thirteen rows of thirty-three Kwannons were placed in their niches, a thousand was thought to be infinitude, but devout Buddhists added one more for good measure. I noticed a tiny, kimono-clad figure contemplating them. She looked as immovable as the statues. When we returned an hour later, she was still in the same spot.

I was melting in the heat. A dry shirt on my back had become a novelty. We stopped frequently for refreshments — crushed ice flavored with strawberry and *ame*, a sticky sweet. Kozo said it was seaweed dipped in jam. It was sold by a storyteller who stood on a box, blowing a bugle to attract customers. He illustrated narratives by slipping a series of pictures in a large frame and imitating animals and birds. The youngsters were captivated.

"*Yie, yie!*" Kozo objected to my photographing the Heian Jingu Shrine. The eighth-century scarlet structure with checkerboard features and a blue-green tile roof was gaudy and garish, but I wanted a picture of it because of its antiquity. Mitsuko made up for my disappointment by finagling two young Shinto nuns into posing. They looked more like geishas in their white blouses and salmon skirts, wistaria in their hair.

Kozo nudged me at that moment, indicating a beautiful girl in a lilac kimono splashed with gold dragons. Above the whitewashed face the black, lacquered wig was spangled with tiny silver bells and fans. She walked like a queen. Evidently she was on her way to some *ochaya* to perform the tea ceremony, since geishas don't wear traditional costumes during the daytime. Kozo said that the famous geisha houses were to be found in the Gion quarter on the west bank of the Kamo River. Fagged though I was, I was all for sampling the Gion.

Mitsuko looked pained. "No time for geisha today. We see next Higashi Hongarji *tera*."

That temple proved to be the most elaborate of all Buddhist temples. We signed the register (mine the only Western signature), and the chief priest asked us inside. He turned out to be related to Dave's foster father, leader of the influential Jodo-Shinshu sect. His wife gave us *ocha* and a fan, then they showed us the huge temple compound, which included a beautiful gateway, a founder's temple, another large one of the Lord Buddha, and a theater for Noh drama. It was here that some of Marlon Brando's scenes for *Sayonara* had been shot.

In the main temple the priest pointed out the ropes, made of women's hair, that had hauled the heavy timbers into place. There were fifty-two, the longest rope thirty-six feet and weighing twenty-three hundred and thirty-four pounds. How many poor peasants had sacrificed their tresses to the building of these holy places?

Our last temple, Kiyomizu, was perched on a cliff. Nearby we got a fine panoramic view of Kyoto from the high wooden platform of the observatory. There was Kyoto nestling in the valley under a brilliant blue sky, with pagodas, shrines and temples and elaborate gardens stretching out for miles. On my right was the Ginkakuji or Silver Pavilion, famous for its sand garden, where women were raking the sand, swept in spiral designs to suggest mountain-ocean harmony. Enough beauty here for a lifetime of memories, enough gold and ivory to feed and house all Asia!

"Pinch me, somebody!" I cried, wishing I had a wide-angle telephoto lens.

Mitsuko did so, laughing like a child. "Near here is Maruyama Park where cherry brossom *matsuri* cerebrated in spring. You come back?"

"*Tabun* — maybe, but I doubt it." I saw her smile fade.

We had chalked up three shrines and seven temples, trudging at least five miles in the hot sun. I felt as languid as a lizard. After driving to a market place in Kyoto, we bought a huge watermelon. The little schoolgirl was shocked when Kozo split it open on an ancient tomb, but she laughed at my joke about eating, drinking and washing your face all at the same time.

As we passed the Catholic church downtown, she told me about St. Francis Xavier and his valiant efforts to introduce Christianity into Japan in 1549. The people never forgot this great missionary, although Catholic priests weren't permitted in Japan until after the treaty with Perry was signed in 1854.

It was in the Nishijin, Kyoto's shopping quarter and art center, that she did me a last good turn. After watching artisans making pottery and carving exquisite objects, we wandered through the bazaars. I saw a lovely hanging scroll in a shop window — a Kabuki Yaegake Princess painted on silk. The *kakemono* was marked Y1850 (about five dollars). I had only seventeen hundred yen in my pocket and asked Kozo to bargain with the shopkeeper. He refused, but Mitsuko said eagerly, "I am happy to be to you of service." I gave her the money. When she came out with the scroll, she looked as thrilled as I felt.

"I want so much to see your country," she said in a hushed voice, as we drove to the railroad station. Then she told me that she had decided to try for an AFS grant.

"I hope you make it," I said warmly, shaking hands. "Thank you for everything, Mitsuko. You gave me lots of pleasure. I'll be writing you. *Sayonara!*" I waved at her through the rear window of the car. She was a dear. I had grown quite fond of her.

XIV
PEACE AND WAR

"A good buy!" Mrs. Okajima congratulated me on getting a rare bargain. Kashu Kikuchi was a famous artist from Kyoto. Then she sighed. "This summer go too fast. In few weeks you gone."

"Don't remind me of it," I said dismally.

Tomorrow, August 6, was the anniversary of the A-bomb. She said she had often wondered how Americans felt about Pearl Harbor. I in turn tried to imagine how she felt about American reprisals. Hiroshima and Nagasaki had been devastated in a matter of seconds, with almost one hundred thousand lives lost. Bomb survivors were still succumbing to atomic sickness, and one in every six babies was deformed or stillborn.

Dave had told me that strangers called on him in Fukui, bringing memorial pamphlets with grisly pictures of Hiroshima victims and asking why Americans had committed this crime against mankind. He replied that he wasn't responsible for his country's foreign policy during the war, then pointed out that, dreadful though it was, the A-bomb had spared untold numbers of lives, making for a speedy, face-saving surrender.

That Tuesday passed quietly. My foster parents tactfully refrained from reminding me of its significance. It was I who broached the subject at dinner. All summer long I had seen people at various railroad stations signing petitions against H-bomb tests. "They must have collected millions of signatures by now," I said.

Mr. Okajima nodded. "Soon we send petitions to Russia, too." He spoke in a subdued tone, looking as somber as his black *yukata*. "What else can we do? Japan is a poor country squeezed between two titanic Communist nations."

"It doesn't seem possible that it happened so many years ago," I said, as the *neesan* brought tea and rice.

"*Hai, hai.*" Mrs. Okajima laid down her fan and began counting on her fingers. "August six, Hiroshima; August eleven, Nagasaki." Then she described the holocaust. They had been living in Nagasaki, where Mr. Okajima had charge of large shipbuilding yards. People had begun to flee their homes in panic after Hiroshima was bombed. When the Allies issued a warning that Nagasaki would be doomed also unless Japan surrendered, my foster parents fled to Tokyo. There they learned that Mr. Okajima's sister had been killed and everything destroyed.

"Everybody run but nowhere to go. Hide under stones. Much hurtings and killings. All terrible — "

It was painful watching her grope for words to express the anguish and horror of that scene. There was no trace of bitterness in her manner. Just sadness. She really lived up to her motto, "To make the world more wonderful!"

"I hope never happen again." She took a deep breath. "America and Japan now friends, *ne?* No more war; onry *yūjō* — friendship."

I sat with lowered eyes while Mr. Okajima described Hiroshima's reconstruction. Today only one partly ruined building stood there as a reminder that war doesn't pay. You could see it through the big stone arch of the Peace Monument. On August 11, a day of national prayer, people would gather early in the morning for the memorial service — about thirty thousand, carrying green wreaths and incense sticks to Nakajima Park, where the unidentified victims were buried in a big round grass mound. The bell would toll and after a moment's silence the mayor would release hundreds of white doves. Buddhist priests would then begin chanting prayers and continue praying all day, until the sun went down.

"There is no answer to A-bomb," he said impressively, after an eloquent silence. "Now that is already obsolete. We have weapons so terrible no nation can win. Our samurai commit *hara-kiri* when Emperor broadcast surrender, but whole world commit suicide if bomb-testing not stop soon." He took off his horn-rimmed glasses and rubbed his eyes wearily. "You will be diplomat some day. You may make big decisions. Your generation must work for peace."

I nodded as I began eating cold rice.

After that evening's revelation the Okajimas meant even more to me than before. It was the last time I saw my foster father. I was disappointed to find that he wasn't on the train next day. I thought he would be going back to Tokyo with us. I hadn't even said good-by, much less thanked him for his hospitality.

When I strolled into the third-class coach, I found our two Joyces with Kate Lowry. They were going to Tokyo to attend the International Party on the ninth. Then, at Nagoya, Elizabeth Titus climbed aboard. Mrs. Okajima had to retrieve me for lunch. I lost all sense of time, swapping experiences with them.

Arriving in Tokyo at four o'clock, we were met by the press and a few other AFSers. After half an hour of excited chatter, the group broke up and I returned to Nishi-Ogikubo with my family. Haru-san greeted us with a radiant smile. We practically fell into each other's arms.

Before I had my bath I read a stack of mail, which included a postcard from an older friend of mine in Boston. Larry wrote that he was dating a Japanese girl he had met at Boston University.

I expected to hear Tomo's voice when the phone rang after dinner and Kozo called me. Instead, Rai's vibrant bass came over the wire like a sonic smack.

"Jim Hauhart's in Tokyo and we're welcoming a batch of Asiatic AFSers at Haneda Airport tomorrow morning around four-thirty. They're returning from the States. Are you game?"

"Sure thing." I hung up, groaning. I had never felt less like going anywhere, but this was in a good cause. So, much to my foster mother's dismay, I threw myself together, left the house and hopped a train to Tokyo.

At Rai's home in Okubo I learned that the AFS char-
tered plane wouldn't arrive until eight next morning. It
seems there were technical difficulties. We were too keyed
up to sleep, so we decided to show Jim the hot spots in
Shinjuku. "In case we get separated," said Rai, "we'll meet
at The Black Rose."

The section we explored was the underworld of opium
dens, dives, brothels, criminal hide-outs and cheap strip-
tease joints. In the red-light district we saw rows of flimsy
shacks, each with a girl beckoning coyly, and pimps shouting, "*Oi, America-jin!*" Sudden cries of "*Junsa, inu* (cops,
dogs) sped along the grapevine. In a flash every sliding door
was eased shut and the streets cleared.

We were meandering through a motley crowd in one of
the countless alleys when somehow we got separated. I
found myself conspicuously alone — closed in, for the first
time, by alien faces. No Japanese would dream of attacking
an American, but I felt threatened. Switch-blade gangs
roamed the streets, wearing blue suits with peg trousers,
tight-fitting pink shirts, black leather jackets, and their hair
slicked up into high pompadours. There were more than
four hundred and fifty such gangs in Tokyo.

Chills chased up my spine at the thought of being stranded
in this section of grubby coffeehouses and dingy shops
smelling of incense and fried fish. Shadowy figures were
slinking in doorways and everyone looked sinister to me. It
had begun to pour as I searched for my friends. I tried to
keep up my courage by whistling Kozo's favorite tune,
"Just Walkin' in the Rain." We had been warned not to
speak to strangers at night, but I was desperate. So I button-

holed a sandwich-man advertising a *tempura* restaurant, and in fractured Japanese asked him if he could direct me to The Black Rose. He said he had never heard of the place, but he tried for at least half an hour to find me a cab.

I turned a corner and heard outcries and angry shouts. Under the dim street lamp I saw half a dozen hooligans mauling a man in a light suit. I was about to turn back when I recognized the lone contestant. It was my friend, Tomo. He was getting a real clobbering. Fists flailed, legs tangled, heads bumped, and no police in sight to stop the slaughter. Not that the *junsa* could have done anything. They were powerless against those gangs.

For a moment I stood paralyzed. Then I swallowed a large lump of fear and walked toward the ruckus, calling Tomo. It worked like magic. There were shouts of *"Oi, oi, America-jin!"* In a jiffy the hoods had melted into the darkness with angry rumblings of *"Baka."*

Tomo's amazement was almost comical. "Pete, you old so-and-so, what are you doing here?" He was reeling like a punch-drunk prize fighter, and began folding up when I grabbed his arm.

"Let's get out of this rain." I helped him into a shabby little café, where he collapsed in a chair. My handsome Nisei was a mess. His summer fatigues were mud-spattered and bloody, his right eye black and blue, his nose a red blob. Poor Tomo — born to trouble! I asked the waitress for a moist cloth, hot coffee and a raw steak. She didn't understand my Japanese, but his shiner was clue enough, and she bustled off shaking her head dismally.

"You need a doctor, Tomo?"

"No, I'm all right." He leaned back, trying to stop the nosebleed. His face, ordinarily a golden tan, was now ghastly green.

"Sure no bones broken?"

He grinned feebly. "No bones. Just my ticker."

"You certainly had spunk taking on six goons! How did the slogging match start?"

"I'm hazy about it. I came here trying to forget my troubles, and they just got in my hair. Guess they don't like Nisei."

"You're lucky they didn't slash your throat."

"Thanks to you."

"Don't thank me. I was too scared to do a thing."

"Okay?" The waitress had brought our order, hovering over Tomo as he clapped the raw meat to his eye. His free hand trembled so much he spilled the coffee.

"Tomo, I felt like a heel turning you down the day you phoned, but the Okajimas were waiting for me in the car. I tried to reach you from Osaka. The hotel clerk said you had checked out, so I left a message — "

"*Checked* out? Oh, these polite Nips!" He gave a short laugh, grimacing with pain. "I landed from the frying pan in the fire — I mean the cooler. That's when I sent you that S.O.S."

I stared at him. "What are you talking about?"

"Remember the day you saw me taking flowers to Miss Tashagi in Shonan?" He heaved a sigh. "Well, I thought I was doing fine. She seemed interested — sweet, friendly, always with the welcome mat out. But I couldn't get anywhere with her strait-laced parents. They fixed things so I never saw her alone. With Mama-san sitting there like a hawk, what could we talk about except the weather? Though I don't think she understood my Japanese or my English. She couldn't make head or tail out of me."

"What about Kiku's kid brother?"

"I never saw him around." Tomo shrugged. "She knew he liked me and I suppose it was bad enough having to be nice to me on his account. That damned *on!* I should've seen I was gate-crashing." He fumbled for a cigarette, which I lit for him. "The more Kiku's parents cooled off, the more I wanted her. I thought she really liked me. Anyhow I had to find out, and fast. There wasn't time to go through any long-winded courtship shenanigans. My furlough's up August 25.

"So one night I went to Shonan with the idea of talking her into eloping. I'd downed a little bottled courage and felt cocksure. I had to keep Mama-san from nosing in, so went around the back way through the garden. It was about nine-thirty, and there was a full moon. Very romantic. I was shinning up a tree to knock on Kiku's window when I heard a woman next door screeching for the cops. Real hysterical. Took me for a prowler. Seems there'd been a robbery in the neighborhood — "

"Gosh, what rotten luck! What happened then?"

"Before I knew it, the *junsa* were pussyfooting around with their silly lanterns and fans. It was hilarious. I couldn't make them understand my intentions were honorable. My Japanese isn't too hot even when I'm calm. Well, they whistled up the M.P.'s and I was hustled off to the clink." He was seething. "Probably the first time a Nisei was ever in jail. None of my people in Cal ever ran foul of the law. It was always the Chinese with their tong wars."

"Whew! You took a long chance, doing a Romeo and Juliet with the daughter of such a conservative family."

"Yeh. Guess I'm not cut out for a Romeo. Well, now I know my place. I found out what I am. Not a burglar but a barbarian. That's what the Tashagis think of me. Mr. Tashagi's secretary slipped me that info when he fished me out of the pokey." Tomo thrust out his jaw. "I'm cured but good. Don't ever want anything more to do with Japanese girls. As they say here, 'It's better to be the head of a sardine than the tail of a sea bream!'" He gulped his coffee and took the raw beef off his eye. The swelling had gone down a little, but it was still bloodshot.

For all his swagger about being cured, I felt he was still carrying the torch.

"Here's a laugh. I bought Kiku an engagement ring — even had her initials engraved on it. Set me back plenty." He looked despondent. "Now what do I do?"

"Don't do anything reckless. Don't blow town. I have a hunch you'll be glad things didn't work out with Kiku. You wouldn't have made a go of it with her." I got up. "Are you free Saturday?"

"Free as a cooked goose," he replied morosely. "Why?"

"Where are you staying?"

"At the Y.M.C.A."

"Okay, I'll call you. Now I must run." He winced when I clapped him on the shoulder. "Take care of that shiner. So long!"

This time I succeeded in getting a cab. "The Black Rose,

please." The sandwich-man had vanished, my Good Samaritan going unthanked. I had no idea what to do about Tomo. I wasn't old or wise enough to solve his problem. He was chasing rainbows. Besides, romance was out of my line — at least at present. There was just one person I felt would be a safe confidante — Ohana. She was a grand girl and she knew something about America.

When I walked into The Black Rose, shouts of relief went up from the fellows. "Where in blazes have you been? What happened, Pete? We were just going to send out a Saint Bernard!"

"I got lost." I shed my soggy raincoat. "Any coffee brewing?" My experience with Tomo had left me weak and shaky.

I made the mistake of ordering a hamburger. Rai grinned when the waitress brought a veal cutlet between two biscuits. "I should have warned you to stick to Japanese fare."

After half an hour's relaxation I felt more like myself, although going without sleep was a frightening thought. At dawn we emerged from that dark hole in the wall, blinking like owls. The streets and shops, bustling a few hours ago, were now practically deserted, and the occasional clatter of *geta* on cobblestones sounded ominous to my jangled nerves. In the interurban to Haneda I stretched out on a bench and took a cat nap while the fellows laced into Stephen Foster songs — "Old Black Joe," "My Old Kentucky Home," melodies loved by the Japanese.

The only sign of life at the International Airport — a large, white modern building — was a snack vender. We had sandwiches and coffee, then sprawled out on the wide, luxurious sofas in the lobby. When I woke up, people had begun dribbling in out of the rain — families and friends of incoming AFSers. They waited patiently and sleepy-eyed, listening to short speeches by Rai and Mr. Iweyama from the Ministry of Education.

At eight-fifteen, umbrellas went up and we walked out on the observation platform to greet the batch of smiling teen-agers who spilled out of the silver ship — about sixty Japanese, Pakistani, Indonesian and Filipino returnees. Some of them sang "Dixie" and waved small Confederate flags. Others wore cowboy hats, and both boys and girls lugged teddy bears and jumbo-sized dolls.

There was no kissing or embracing among the Japanese families who were reunited after a year. They merely smiled and bowed, but oh, their happy faces! I recognized a couple of Japanese girls who had visited my family in Gloucester in the spring. They looked amazingly fresh considering their long trip, although one girl confessed to feeling tottery. "The trip from Minnesota took thirty-six hours. We had a forced landing at Anchorage — "

"But also a marvelous venison dinner and a bus tour," her friend bubbled.

During the long wait through customs and the inevitable baggage mix-ups we all posed for pictures, taken by the newly arrived AFS photographer. Then, after we had helped Japanese returnees load their family cars, Rai flagged a *kamikaze*. I had the honor of sitting in the suicide seat, beside the driver. While he honked, started, stopped, dodged, swerved, and hurtled through the early morning traffic, I clung to the meter, petrified. Whenever another car side-swiped ours I shielded my face, gibbering and praying.

"See you at the International Party tomorrow," Rai said at Okubo Station, where I was dropped off — in a semiconscious state.

I caught the ten-thirty A.M. back to Nishi-Ogikubo, my head like a pumpkin about to burst. Both Mrs. Okajima and Haru-san met me at the door with murmurs of concern. I must have looked as I felt — hot, tired, sticky, grimy, ready to fall apart. Haru-san took my damp clothes and hurried away to start my bath, while Mrs. Okajima went upstairs to lay out my *futon*.

It seemed like ages since I had hit the sack. But my exertions were in a good cause. Another down payment on my debt to the AFS!

XV
INTERNATIONAL PARTY

The Kiyosumi Garden and Teahouse was a cool and quiet oasis on this hot, hazy afternoon, the roar of traffic muffled. Hard to believe that we were bang in the middle of Tokyo! The sliding doors of the *ochaya* opened on an exquisitely landscaped garden. Japanese lanterns were strung along the trees, and flags of all nations. The long tables set out on a lawn offered a bewildering assortment of pastry, fruits and beverages.

Our host, the Governor of Tokyo, was conspicuous by his absence, but an official from the American Embassy gave the tea party tone. He circulated among the guests — boys in light cord suits, girls charming in their gay prints, the scent they wore mingling with the sweet-smelling flowers and cigarette smoke.

I looked around for Ohana. I had been unable to reach her by phone, and I was anxious to talk to her about Tomo. This was my last chance. The day after tomorrow we'd begin our trip to Northern Honshu. Recent returnees asked us where we came from, hoping that we'd send messages to their American families. "We miss them already." They all raved about the open-hearted generosity of Americans.

An earnest-looking Japanese boy introduced himself, asking timidly for my advice on a personal matter. "I'm very anxious to have an American student spend next summer with my family," said Akira, as we sat in a shady spot by a pond bobbing with water lilies. "We're not rich. Our home is very modest. Do you think an American boy would mind?"

"Mind?" Evidently Akira had been overly impressed by our nation's wealth. "I'd say most American boys would jump at the chance, and the AFS would be delighted. But wouldn't it mean a real sacrifice for your folks?"

"That wouldn't matter. I'd be glad to wash dishes in a restaurant. I want to repay the AFS for my wonderful year in the States."

"Well, I'm sure Rai can arrange it."

"What would an American expect of us?"

I smiled. "You're mixing up the fish and bait. It's rather what you would expect of him. The guest is the one to adjust. That's the whole point of the program."

"But does the AFS consider homes with only one parent? You see, we live in Hiroshima and I lost my mother and two sisters."

"Oh, I'm sorry," I said lamely, my cheeks burning. "Rai could tell you that."

"Now that I've seen America, I want to find homes for American students here." His black eyes followed the movements of a large orange butterfly. "It's funny, when I was in the States I was too shy to mix with other AFSers, although I've always been interested in Americans. My mother always dressed me in *yōfuku* — Western clothes. I'm eighteen and I've never worn a *kimono* or *yukata*. When she was killed, all Americans were my enemies. But now they're my friends. I want to do everything I can to help build peace."

Just then I caught sight of Ohana. I asked Akira to excuse me.

"Gosh, I'm glad to see you, Ohana!" The simple white dress she wore set off her pale-gold skin and black hair, but her face looked strained. "I was afraid you — "

"I've been visiting Mother at the hospital," she said in a low voice. "It was even more painful than I expected. She's so changed I wouldn't have known her. What she went through — "

"It's over now, Ohana. She's getting the care she needs. Don't think of the past. Let's have fun. Come on, we'll get something to eat."

"Well," she said with a ghost of a smile, as we sat near a dwarfed tree, sipping lemonade and eating big juicy peaches, "is Kozo still pining for Koharu?"

"I wish I knew! I'm not so worried about him, though. He'll make out. Look, Ohana, I know you're terribly upset about your mother, but perhaps if you could help someone else — A friend of mine is in a real spot. He's an oddball, a Nisei G.I., here on furlough from Korea. He doesn't belong in America and he's not happy in Japan."

143

"That I can understand. Our people dislike the Nisei and make them look silly every chance they get. At bottom we envy those Japanese born in a free world."

"I can't understand why Tomo didn't marry a Nisei. He thinks so highly of them. Anyhow, he's been treated like a second-class citizen all his life. He tried to buck the whole social system, getting involved in a romance with a beautiful girl who's out of his class. Her family's very old-fashioned, and they threw him out on his ear. Kiku Tashagi — "

"Why, one of my friends knows her. Wasn't her father something or other to the Mikado? Yes, she's a beauty — the type that is painted on fans — but she's not very bright."

"I'm seeing Tomo tomorrow. I wonder if you'd like to come along."

Ohana nodded. "He sounds interesting, though hardly typical of the Nisei."

"I'm sure of that, but he's sincere and he's got spunk — the sort who crawls out on a limb and saws it off. He needs a friend, and he may take your mind off your own troubles. You understand this is all confidential."

"Strictly *entre nous.*" She agreed to meet me at a coffee shop in Ikebukuro.

I was sorry she couldn't go to the Kabuki Theater that afternoon. She needed distraction badly. We were to meet at the Imperial — Rai, Pete Martin and his Japanese friend, Mako. When we got there, I phoned Tomo at the Y.M.C.A., setting up a date for the next day. I didn't mention Ohana.

The Kabuki-za near the Ginza gave two performances daily — one from twelve to four, another from five to

144

Town and Country Life

Building and Begging

nine P.M. We hoped to make the latter. While we waited in the lobby for Mako, Rai gave us the highlights.

"The word means eccentric, off balance. It's hard to describe, and it'll seem strange to you. There's nothing like it in the whole world. What you get out of it depends on what you bring to it. It's a mixture of pageant, ballet and opera — music, dance, drama. The acting is very subtle. Everything is expressed in symbols. A kimono spread out on the stage, for instance, represents a dead woman."

"Is Kabuki like the Noh drama?" I asked him.

"Well, they're both forms of classical drama, but Noh is even less realistic — more symbolic and stylized than Kabuki. Noh is for the bluebloods, Kabuki for the masses. All Kabuki actors are men, you know, and they have feminine ways down cold — walk, manner, gestures, everything! They study for years to impersonate a woman. They're so perfect that geisha girls go to Kabuki plays just to learn proper deportment. Our greatest star now is Nosuke — "

"I met him backstage," Pete Martin interrupted. "He let me watch him put on his costume and make-up. Wait till you see the gorgeous outfits! Some of them are two hundred and fifty years old."

"The plays are either historical or legendary," Rai continued. "Feudal dramas with sword duels and plenty of gore. Some plays are romantic, some comedies. The program tells the story, but you should really know the symbolism to enjoy it. Tonight's play is about a geisha girl who commits suicide."

I slapped my knee. "Lay on, Macduff!"

"We can't go without Mako." Rai frowned, glancing at

the door. "Let me tell you about the *jojuri* — a kind of Greek chorus made up of singers and musicians. They sit on their heels at one side of the stage, chanting the dialogue or stressing some high moment in the drama. They also furnish sound effects. Another thing. The stagehands wear black — they're supposed to be invisible — and walk on in the middle of the play to change the actors' costumes and the props."

I was fascinated. "Arthur Lederman says there's a board-walk — "

"That's right. Actors use the *hana-michi* — the Flower Bridge — for entrances and exits, for processions — or ghosts."

Mako hadn't turned up by six-thirty. We were all chafing. How much more of Kabuki would we have to miss? We killed half an hour playing *pachinko*, Pete Martin winning some Peace cigarettes. We were really annoyed to find no Mako when we got back, so we decided to have dinner at the Imperial. We had given him up by eight P.M., when he rushed in, out of breath and complaining bitterly. It seems our signals had got crossed. He had been hunting for us all this time.

"Well, at least we'll catch the last act." Rai hailed a cab.

Behind a typical Japanese façade was a luxurious lobby filled with souvenir shops and tearooms. The modern, air-conditioned Kabuki-za accommodated fifteen hundred, and it was packed with a shirt-sleeve audience, mostly middle-aged, with a sprinkling of students.

Ours were the worst seats at the back of the house. All I could take in was the magnificent costumes and scenery. The actors moved like molasses on that eighty-foot stage. It took an eternity for them to make an entrance. The stilted falsetto voices grated on my ears, and so did the singing. (Later Rai laughed at me for accusing his people of having no ear for music and singing off key. Apparently their quarter-tone scale is a subtle refinement.)

Mako translated the story in his terse, staccato fashion. "Geisha commit suicide because her rover turn out to be dragon. Dragon srain by sacred mountain."

I watched a grotesque figure wearing a fleecy wig that got tangled up behind his back. "What's he supposed to be — man or woman?" I asked in a stage whisper.

"Iss man but awso woman. Iss very sacred. Iss hory mountain."

The actor was giving off a banshee-like wail, alternately rising on his clogs and shrinking to midget size, all the while busy swishing a gigantic papier-mâché sword. I wondered why he didn't cut off his head and get it over with.

"Mountain mad at wicked dragon," Mako explained.

Seeing no dragon anywhere, I nudged Mako. He looked at me with a long-suffering air. "Sh, dragon he spirit. Now mountain to cut off dragon's head. Iss making spell."

The keening went on and on, the high, eerie sound bouncing off the ceiling. Meanwhile, Old Man Mountain slashed around on his knees with the sword.

Mako touched my elbow. "Iss praying forgiveness to spirit of dragon."

This was too much for me. I stopped straining my imagination. After Rai's big build-up — I never did see the geisha girl. But I did get a vicarious thrill watching the audience. They were completely carried away, some sobbing audibly, more reverent than any temple worshipers, even more excited than baseball spectators. Mako kept hissing, "Iss so sad, iss so beautiful!" To me, it meant as much as a Punch and Judy show.

So I checked off Kabuki, the second main objective of my Oriental junket. Fuji-san was still hearsay, while geisha girls were still a tantalizing myth.

XVI
CUPID IS DE TROP

I started out next day for Ikebukuro with an uneasy feeling that I was rushing in where angels feared to tread. Would Tomo resent Ohana and feel that I had betrayed his confidence? Well, it was too late to turn back now.

The *Kohi-shopu* was a fancy place — medieval German architecture, plush carpets, palm trees and a goldfish pool. Beethoven was cooking. The hi-fi cabinet, designed like a pipe organ, must have cost the proprietor about four hundred thousand yen — eleven hundred dollars. What a background for Tomo and his troubles!

Ohana appeared, looking more cheerful today. Charming in a rose-colored dress, she smiled up at me through her thick lashes. "Your friend hasn't come yet?"

"He ought to be here soon." I almost wished he wouldn't show up. What if he was in one of his rambunctious moods? I was on tenterhooks as he blew in, looking anything but jaunty. His shiner had faded, but he was still licking his wounds. When I introduced him, he eyed Ohana suspiciously, then glanced at me as much as to say, "Hey, what gives?" My heart sank. He was going to be difficult.

An attractive hostess led us to a table in a cubicle, where we could talk freely. My guests ordered coffee, I a mint ice-cream soda. Tomo lit Ohana's cigarette, sizing her up warily. I broke the ice, rambling on about my Kabuki experience.

"It's my own fault that I couldn't enjoy it. I should have boned up on it beforehand."

"Shucks, I don't get that high-class stuff either." Tomo rubbed his chin reflectively. "I like burlesque shows." He guffawed. "Reminds me of something a pal in Korea told me. During the Occupation he saw a burlesque here in Tokyo on Christmas Eve. Cuties came onstage in G strings and carrying lighted candles. Must have started a riot when they began singing, 'Siren Night, Hory Night'!"

He was testing Ohana to see if she was shock-proof. The twinkle in her dark eyes reassured him. He grinned.

"I love vaudeville myself," she said. "To me it's duck soup, as Peter-chan would say. I was lucky in seeing a performance in the States before that stage art became obsolete."

"So you're a returnee!" Tomo's eyes flickered. "Where did you live?"

"In California."

"No kidding! That's where I was born and raised." He was slowly dropping his guard. "This is my first look at Japan. All the guys in my outfit in Korea took it for granted that I knew Japan from stem to stern. Just because my eyes slant they expected me to tell them everything from bowing to the tea ceremony. 'Listen, buddy,' I'd say, 'I hate tea. Beer I'll drink, but I hate tea.'" He rumpled his hair in exasperation. "In the States I'm not a Yank, and here I'm a no-body. I just don't belong anywhere. You might say home's anywhere I hang my hat."

She raised an eyebrow. "Your hat, yes, but what about your heart?"

He looked blank. "What do you mean, Ohana — I may call you Ohana?"

"Why not?" She took a sip of coffee. "You can be up-rooted and transplanted again and again and still grow, as long as you belong to yourself. Being an international has its advantages, you know." She tilted her head. "You learn to understand the other person's viewpoint, for one thing."

This was easier than I had thought. I sat back and lis-tened.

"I'm not sure the Japanese want to be understood," said Tomo. "They're as deep as icebergs — nine-tenths sub-merged. Never take off their masks. That's why the Noh drama is so popular. The actors all wear masks. You of-fended?"

"Not at all." She smiled. "But we are trying to dig our-selves out of that iceberg, out of the past."

Tomo hitched his chair closer to hers. "Have another cof-fee and some pastry. This is on me, Pete." He was becom-ing more and more expansive.

"No more, thank you." Ohana excused herself, getting up to look for the powder room.

"You old so-and-so, holding out on me!" He slapped me on the shoulder. "She's the real goods. Understands a guy. Think I could date her? She's probably loaded with men friends."

"No, she really likes you, Tomo. If she didn't, she would have said polite nothings." When I told him briefly what Ohana had been through and how her health suffered in consequence, his sympathies were stirred.

"Poor kid, I wish I could help."

As soon as she returned, he astonished me by spilling the beans. "You're a sensible girl, Ohana. Maybe you can tell me — something happened to a friend of mine. A knucklehead like me who got tangled up with one of those rich and ritzy Japanese families. Fell for a beautiful gal, and all he got was a black eye and a busted heart. You think he ought to fight for her or just drown his sorrows in beer?"

Ohana's smile was inscrutable. "Something like that might happen to someone like you." Her long, sensitive fingers played with her coffee spoon. "Might it be the wrong girl perhaps? I heard about a very gallant G.I. who befriended Kiku Tashagi's little brother — "

"Don't tell me you know her!" Tomo's jaw dropped.

"No, but I have a friend who does. The Tashagis are a distinguished family, but they live completely in the past and think only about rituals and traditions. Kiku's got beauty and a rich father, but those things happened to her. She didn't create them. All she knows is flower arrangements and performing the tea ceremony. What sort of a life could you have made with such a hothouse plant? She doesn't want to be rescued from her prison. She's happy — "

"Because she never tasted freedom, you mean." He tugged at his ear. "I suppose I was a sucker."

"No, you were pretty heroic and a gentleman, but foolish to think that Kiku could possibly be right for you."

"Well, it's a relief to meet a square shooter. You've got brains and you think for yourself. At least you don't hide behind a fan, cooing and giggling."

I was shut out. They had forgotten my very existence. Obviously Tomo didn't need me any more. I felt rather miffed. But then the role of *nakōdo* is always a thankless one.

"Sorry," I said rather stiffly, when Tomo asked me to dinner. "The *Asahi Evening News* is feeding all of us AFSers tonight. Also I have to pack for tomorrow's train tour."

"How about you?" He hung on Ohana's answer.

"I'd like to very much, thank you." She smiled up at him demurely.

They were nice enough to let me pick up the tab, after all. Tomo clasped his hands over his head like a prize fighter, as Ohana preceded us out of the coffee shop. Well, he could take it from there. I had done my bit. Exit Cupid.

Several hours later, Kozo saw me off at the station in Nishi-Ogikubo with a broad grin and a glib, "See you rater, arrigator!" His mother had disconcerted me by making light of my forthcoming ordeal — keeping all-night vigil at Ueno Station so that our AFS coeds could get seats on the nine A.M. train to Matsushima. Our departure would coincide with the *O-Bon* Festival up north, the day when city-dwellers visited their country relatives.

"Many peoperu go to beeg *matsuri* in Matsushima." She laid both hands against her cheek. "You sleep so by newspapah Watanabe-san put on floor near train — "

And that's how it was. At one A.M., Rai, Pete Martin

and myself spread newspapers on the platform at Ueno, although we weren't the only ones staking a claim. The place had been converted into a communal bedroom, young and old stretching out on the cement and using their bulky *furoshiki* as pillows.

I didn't get much shut-eye on this Night of the Great Insomnia, but Rai took it all in stride. He could sleep standing up. Typically Japanese, he had been trained early to doze through all kinds of noises and jogglings, strapped as he was to his mother's back. But I'll bet he never before made such a sacrifice for the sake of *les femmes!* It was an eerie experience. We wandered around the station, drinking coffee and talking to the beggars we saw huddled in corners and tunnels.

By seven-thirty A.M. the station resembled an anthill in wild disorder. There was a frantic rush for the coaches marked "For Sendai," and a chorus of "*Dozo . . . Sumimasen . . . Oi, oi . . . Arigato . . .*" Our coeds arrived at the very last minute with Yoshi, the Japanese AFS correspondent. Two other returnees turned up, then the AFS photographer and a woman reporter from the *Asahi*, whose guests we were.

As the train got under way, we began whooping it up, our Japanese families and friends waving a sentimental good-by. Mrs. Hideki Kikuchi, the retired movie actress, ran gracefully beside the coach, holding Arthur's hand through the window until the train gathered speed.

"My foster mother's much too beautiful," he sighed. "When she called me her darling and I called her my dear, my foster father made a great show of glaring at me."

XVII
GRAND TOUR

A perfect August day with a cool breeze and the sky brilliant sapphire! After the eight-hour train ride to Sendai, the boat trip across Matsushima Bay to the Isle of Pines was a refreshing change. There were nearly three hundred of these islands made of volcanic rock. The tides had etched them into fantastic caves and arches. Each one was a gem, the tiniest like a miniature Japanese garden floating in a blue saucer.

As we shucked our shoes at the Kanko Hotel, Kate Lowry sighed, "Thank goodness mine don't look quite so conspicuous here! The day I arrived in Japan, I had a fit when I saw my foster father's shoes were three inches shorter than mine!"

"That's nothing." Dave Brudnoy flashed his sun goggles at her. "At least you're no skyscraper. I literally hit the ceiling every time I walk through a door. One day when the doctor came to take a crick out of my back, he had to stand on a chair to pull on my arm."

That evening we watched an unforgettable sight from the balcony of the hotel. Thousands of *O-Bon* merrymakers swarmed the beaches, while rows of *sampans* rocked at anchor, their lanterns glowing red, pink, purple. In the center of the beach was a high stage (*yagura*), where girls in striped and flowered *yukatas* performed the Bon Dance under swinging lanterns and to the accompaniment of *samisen*, drums and firecrackers.

Joyce Bartschi, our Mormon coed, was awestruck. "It's like something out of a fairy tale!"

The girls were dismayed to find only one tub at the Kanko. We settled the Order of the Bath by the paper-scissors-stone game — *jan-ken-po.*

"Gentlemen first," crowed Arthur, defeating Joyce Stallsmith. That was all right in Japan but a travesty of American manners.

Dave was cocky about winning the endurance contest we staged later in the girls' room. "I practically spent the summer on my knees. One night I crouched for three hours. When I got up, I collapsed."

Much to Dave's chagrin, Yoshi won the match. We got bored long before the end of two hours.

The next day the train carried us south to the small town of Itoigawa, where a new railroad station was to be christened. The streets were strung with gay banners and lanterns, the shining white station itself decorated with bright posters and garlands.

"*Sushin?*" asked Dave, aiming his camera at a shriveled old man, who looked like a gnome among the flowers.

"*Daijōbu*" (all right). He nodded with a toothless smile.

156

Sightseeing

Asakusa

Shinto Nuns

Trash Collector

The Married Rocks

Ginza Butterflies

Fashion Clothes the Earth

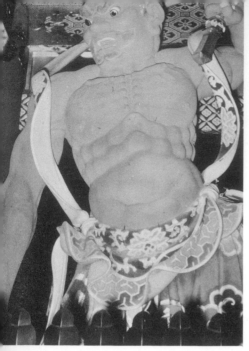

No Fun without Devils

Watermelon, Anyone?

Then, with everything ready for the evening's festivities, came the deluge. We scampered back to the hotel. While Rai was cooking *sukiyaki* over a *hibachi*, a messenger arrived with an invitation. Since the rain had spoiled the outdoor celebration, there would be a jamboree in the town hall, with a special dance given in our honor.

That evening, decked out in our best, we watched eight kimono-clad women do folk dances to the accompaniment of *samisen*, *koto* and drums. We were inspired to put on an American show. Pete Martin and Joyce Stallsmith did the Charleston; Joyce Bartschi and I jitterbugged. We finished with three exaggeratedly low bows, then sent every one into hysterics trying to teach the women the bunny-hop.

We left the hall with their thanks and *Banzai* echoing in our ears. That foreign invasion probably gave them something to talk about for months.

Dave grew more and more excited as the train sped across the Joshin-Etsu Plateau and the Japan Alps toward Fukui. At Kanazawa, a gorgeous-looking girl in a yellow sweater and red skirt came on board and, swishing her long pony tail, presented him with rice cakes (*sembei*).

"Itsuko is a rebel," Dave said later on. "She refuses to wear dumpy school uniforms. Her father's a powerful priest in charge of a super-duper temple compound. There's even a bard's temple for poetry lovers. They live in Matsuto in a fifty-room house with an elegant ebony *benjo*. Don't ask me why, but that *benjo* is reserved for the Emperor's brother exclusively. Just one of those mysteries! Then on the top floor of the mansion there's a dressmaking school — to supplement the family income."

When Itsuko got off at Matsuto, there was Mama-san, smiling broadly and loaded down with boxes of bean cakes for Dave. At Komtasu, three more cousins greeted him with tea and more *O-kashi*. Finally, as the train puffed to a stop at Fukui, we saw his entire foster family ranged along the platform, beaming, bowing, and plying him with enough food and *sake* for all of us.

His relatives were plainly daffy about him. "You know those Buddhist temples are just like our community centers," he said. "They're used for all sorts of things — youth groups, civic rallies, Ladies' Aid meetings, badminton tournaments, pilgrims' sleeping quarters — "

"Why, that's awful!" Elizabeth Titus looked scandalized. "I do think Buddhism is outdated, but using sacred places — "

"Anything that draws young people is valid," Dave said with a shrug. "A Buddhist priest is very obliging. He'll perform a service for anybody that comes along. If he's not home, members of his family take over. When my foster father was in the war, his wife took on his job."

It's impossible to describe the lavish hospitality of the Japanese. They simply couldn't do enough for us. At Hikone, a small town near Lake Biwa, four of us boys were invited to spend the night with Mayor II (pronounced *E*) at his magnificent estate. Rai was overcome by the honor of being a guest of the great-grandson of Naosuke II, who signed the Japan-American Treaty with Commodore Matthew Perry in 1854.

We had dinner at a Japanese restaurant near Hikone Castle and our genial, trim-looking host told us that when the Japanese saw Perry's steamships for the first time, they were so terrified by those "sea monsters" that they plunged into the ocean. Japan had been sealed off from the world before the seventeenth century and trade forbidden until the nineteenth. Westerners were foreign devils and barbarians. The Japanese were slow to appreciate Perry. But once they lost their fears, they overwhelmed him and his crew with hospitality. Just as MacArthur ("Makata") would someday be regarded as a liberator instead of a tyrant.

Before we left Hikone, we gave short talks at the local Rotary Club. The Japanese AFS listed our full names on the program – all but Elizabeth's. The Titus they omitted, evidently feeling that her first name was plenty. On our leaving, there were gifts again – as if they hadn't done enough to help finance our tour!

The *Asahi Evening News* had planned a comprehensive tour – textile, spinning and pottery factories, pearl-diving at Toba, and The Married Rocks at Futamiga-Ura on the Bay of Ise. Roped together, they symbolized the solidity of marriage. (I wondered how Tomo and Ohana were making out.)

On a moonless night we saw a fascinating scene along Nagara River, near Gifu. Fishermen in grass skirts and traditional headgear released a flock of cormorants from fishing-smacks projecting blazing torches over the water. The captive birds wore neck-bands to prevent them from swallowing their quarry, the *ayu*. The river smelt was held in their baggy gullet until disgorged. Winged hunters and fishermen worked together like an inspired team. Rai said that this ancient custom of fishing is the prerogative of just six families in Japan.

On the train bound for Hakone, I got into a heated argument about U.S. politics with Art and Pete Martin. Even Jimmy, absorbed in his new Konica camera, joined the scrap. The girls sensibly kept out of it, Liz reading *The Compassionate Buddha*, while Joyce Bartschi and Kate wrote in their diaries. But they were worried when fellow passengers stared and hissed politely. At length Arthur broke the tension by bawling, "Next station, Confusion!"

Throughout the ten-day tour we kept comparing notes, swapping experiences and pooling impressions. One evening we sat cross-legged on *tatami* in our Hakone hotel room, eating bitter Mandarin oranges around a glowing *hibachi*. Without pulling any punches, here's how we sounded:

Arthur (humble as a penitent monk): I learned one thing from the Japanese — forbearance. When I got here, I thought I was God's gift to Japan. How wrong can you be? For weeks I committed the unforgivable sin of rinsing off the soap in the tub. My family must have spent hours scrubbing the tub and lugging fresh water. But they never said boo. After Rai tipped me off, I noticed happier faces all around. Sometimes such courtesy —

Joyce Bartschi: — is pretty hard to take. I know. My family must have thought I was in mourning, they were so sympathetic. I found out what a dumb bunny I was, sticking my chopsticks straight up in the rice —

Rai (chortling): The way we arrange offerings to the dead.

Joyce: And that wasn't all. I went around wearing the right flap of my kimono over the left. Finally my foster mother asked delicately whom I was mourning.

Dave: You call that a boner? Listen, I goofed all summer long. I used the sacred temple grounds for sun-bathing in my shorts. I know they were shocked, but they just laughed. I caught on in time.

Yoshi (gently): In your heart you meant well. We all understood that.

Dave: My foster father was wonderful — so protective. Never once criticized, no matter what I did. We used to sit up nights, discussing Buddhism and Judaism, all filtered through our dictionaries. The time he spent with me! Why, one evening he took half an hour to explain that a school-teacher was coming a long way just to see me. The visitor arrived and we had an hour of "conversation," neither of us understanding a word. When I think how kind and decent he was —

Joyce Stallsmith: Oh, if only the whole world spoke the same language! I wonder why the Japanese have so much trouble with English.

Dave: Well, it's not compulsory until junior high, you know. There's a school in Fukui that goes in for a whole slew of clubs. One of them is the Broken English Club.

Elizabeth: We ought to start a Broken Japanese Club. Most of us take French in high school, but how many of us can speak it? The schools here impressed me so much. Students work hard, but they're not allowed to speak unless asked, and they never air their views and opinions. Most of the classes are of the lecture type.

Pete Martin: Yes, there's too much cramming and too little chance for developing the imagination.

Peter Bell: I'd like to pay you a tribute, Yoshi. I mean to all Japanese women. You're wonderful. You work like Spartans, you never complain, you're all so gentle and considerate. We hardly know how to thank you. Remember our hostess in Nagoya stopping in the middle of a meal just to fan us? And when we wanted to wash dishes, she was horrified.

Jimmy Hauhart: The patience of the women is unbelievable. Do you know that every single fruit blossom in my foster family's orchard was wrapped in insect-proof paper sacks? All done by women.

Dave: You're so right — about Japanese women, I mean. But it's hard to understand some of the men. In the war our soldiers found out how cruel and arrogant they could be.

Rai (starkly): Yes, war's war! But Westerners don't realize that a lot of so-called Japanese brutality was quite normal by our standards. We're a hardy race. Our soldiers treated the enemy just as they themselves were treated. We can take physical punishment, sleep anywhere, and live on next to nothing. Starvation diets? What about some of our people having to eat rats during the war?

Arthur: That's incredible!

Rai: It's true. Japanese atrocity stories must be taken with a grain of salt.

Dave (earnestly): I wasn't needling, Rai. I can't tell you how much I admire your people's stoicism and courage. You're like the tortoise — patient, philosophical, always rocking back on your feet and forging ahead, but keeping everything hidden under a shell.

Peter Bell: That's it. That's the whole paradox of the Japanese. Kind and indulgent, more than lenient with others but harsh and rigid themselves.

Dave: Rigid and family-bound. My foster brother, Saturo, is a typical Japanese, a wonderful boy. He couldn't be less interested in religion, and yet he's ready to succeed his father as Buddhist priest just so he won't break the seven hundred-year-old Fujii line.

Yoshi: You think this a contradiction? In America I saw also this contradiction, but in another way. I spent a week end in a friend's home. Her mother was most kind and asked many questions about Japan. She said she wished her daughter had such good manners as Japanese girls. Later in my room, Louise said, "Don't pay any attention to Mother. She doesn't mean half what she says. She's just showing off." I was much puzzled.

Rai: While I was in the States, one of my friends took me driving. I heard him argue with his father, who didn't want him to take the car. My friend said, "I'll go eighty in this jalopy just to show the old man where he gets off."

Pete Martin: And did he?

Rai: No, but I was worried. Why should he risk his life just to get even with his father? Didn't he owe his parents respect and obedience?

Yoshi: Perhaps the young people in America try to compete with their parents. They think they can do better.

Here we are content if we can be half as fine. So we accept the guidance of our elders.

Kate: You're right, Yoshi. We could use a little more family feeling. When teen-agers have too much freedom, when they think there's nothing they can't get or do or be, they become confused. So they rebel. You see how I've changed since I came to Japan!

Peter Bell: That explains why we have so much juvenile delinquency. But here it seems that some young people are becoming more like Americans. In certain ways that's good. In others — ? On the whole, I think we've made a good start at getting to know and understand your people, Rai. We can't expect to have all the answers. As you said, 'Give us time!' "

Rai: Japan is like Janus, the Roman god with two faces, who looked both east and west. Our youth is torn between the old and the new culture. Not a promising picture when you think that our generation will be governing Japan in the most difficult age in history! It's too late for *us* to change. We're too set in our ways of thinking and acting. Our only hope is that the children will be taught respect for the individual, which is the core of democracy.

We found good fellowship everywhere and were sped on our way with hearty cries of *"Banzai."* Traveling east on the homeward stretch, I had a presentiment of disturbing news awaiting me in Tokyo. Did it have anything to do with that soothsayer's prediction? At Kamakura, I remembered with amusement my first day in Japan and Kozo's vague, *"Tabun,"* when I asked about the Daibutsu.

Kasuga Shrine

Sumiyoshi Shrine

Daibutsu at Kamakura

A Cemetery — in Tribute to the Dead

This colossal bronze image of Buddha faced the Pacific. It expressed the wisdom of the ages. The eyes, of pure gold, were half closed, the face tranquil and serene, reflecting the rewards of contemplation.

We walked into the hollow figure and climbed into the forehead. Looking through the eyes of the Enlightened One was a profound experience for me. Kipling's lines from *Kim* came to mind:

> Oh ye who tread the Narrow Way
> By Tophet-flare to Judgment Day,
> Be gentle when the heathen pray
> To Buddha at Kamakura!
>
> For whoso will, from Pride released,
> Contemning neither creed nor priest,
> May hear the Soul of all the East
> About him at Kamakura *

* From "Buddha at Kamakura," by permission of Doubleday & Co., Mrs. George Bambridge, Rudyard Kipling's daughter, and Macmillan Co. of Canada.

XVIII
THE TWAIN SHALL MEET

We came back Thursday evening, glad to be home again, sad that our last fling was over. I had collected about a hundred pen pals.

The Okajimas welcomed me as always with deep salaams and broad smiles, Kozo barking a shy "Haro" from the upper teakwood level. Mrs. Okajima handed me a message, marked urgent: "Please call Mr. Tasuki at the International House."

"Hi, Tomo, just got your message. How's everything with you?"

An excited falsetto blasted my ears. "I've been tearing my hair, Pete, afraid you'd miss the greatest day of my life. It's happened, man, it's happened. I still can't believe it. Ohana and I are getting spliced."

I was flabbergasted. "What?" My voice came out in a croak. "Stop pulling my leg."

"I'm not kidding. Drop everything tomorrow afternoon and be at the Meiji Shrine at three sharp. We can't get married without our *nakōdo*."

"I wouldn't miss it for the world!" Stammering congratulations, I hung up in a daze. Tomo married and by a Shinto priest? A Shinto wedding for that maverick? Did this explain my premonition? Hardly. Not this good news.

Mrs. Okajima gave me a quizzical smile when I walked into the den. "You are having good news?"

"The best." She was greatly intrigued when I told her about Tomo and Ohana. After pouring out my impressions and sensations of the train tour, I had a hot bath and went upstairs to open my mail. There were twenty-two letters and another postcard from Larry — a cryptic, "Hi, Pete, you're the one who got to see Japan, but I'm the lucky guy. Japan came to me and she's said yes. So I'm keeping her for the rest of my life. Yours in a rush, Larry."

I wished him happiness, wondering if she was one of us. The AFS had produced a rash of romances. A Japanese girl was engaged to a Swiss boy she had met in the States, a Japanese boy was conducting a courtship by mail with a Finnish girl whom he was planning to meet at the U.N. in 1962.

I got so sleepy after reading a dozen letters that I didn't even glance at the rest. They probably weren't important anyhow. Or so I thought.

Only twice that summer had I slept in a bed. I had acquired good sleeping habits under all conditions and actually preferred my pallet. I had become so "Japonized," even using *r*'s instead of *l*'s, that switching back to American customs and thinking would take conscious effort. Mr. Okajima had complimented me on my grasp of Japanese. "You catch everything."

Kozo hustled me out early next morning for a shopping spree in the Ginza. I had a "sinking fund" of twelve dollars and fifty cents left from our forty-nine-dollar allotment for souvenirs, and it sank still more after I bought a sea-gull brooch for Haru-san, a suitcase large enough to hold the summer's hoard of presents, and a couple of two-dollar color prints at the Watanabe Print Shop. (A Boston art dealer later offered me thirty dollars apiece for them.) I didn't want to borrow cash and add to the white bucket marked "Unpaid Bills," on our Gloucester porch, but I was virtually reduced to a pauper after buying my wedding present for Tomo and Ohana. All newlyweds should start housekeeping with the Goddess of Mercy on their mantelpiece, so I chose a charming little wood carving of Kwannon.

At Tokyo Station I met the other AFSers and we hopped a bus to the Morinaga Dairy Plant, accompanied by the radio, press and TV. Previously the *Asahi* reporters had asked what we missed most in Japan and I had said, "Tall glasses of milk." The result was a frenzied contest. We sat around the table drinking milk and multi-flavored yogurt, while picture bulbs flashed in our faces. I won, downing *eight* pints of yogurt. One thing led to another. After showing us the plant, one of the newest and largest in the world, Morinaga officials said they hoped to underwrite next summer's crop of American AFSers in Japan. Ah, pioneers!

That afternoon, full of yogurt and sentiment, I arrived

at the Maiji Shrine. It was a small wedding. I saw only a scattering of people in the altar-room, the men in conventional black cutaways, the women in dark, printed kimonos. Where was Rai? I sat beside a middle-aged couple wondering if they were Ohana's adopted parents. I couldn't see anyone answering her mother's description. She was probably still in the hospital. As a go-between, I felt pardonably puffed up. Now I also had the responsibility of a *nakōdo* in trying to make the match a success.

Shortly after three o'clock I heard a rustle and stir. Tomo, looking grave and distinguished in a tuxedo, came in and took a chair at the altar. The priest appeared, his gold and silver fan matching his sumptuous robes. His spectacles glittered under a black, high-domed hood. When the bride entered and sat opposite Tomo, the place seemed flooded with sunshine. Ohana looked ethereal and ravishing in a long, ivory brocade kimono lined with red satin. Her *obi* was looped high in the back in a butterfly bow. Attached to her headdress, an elaborate wig, was a band of red and white silk, called a "horn-hider." The implication? A wife must never show jealousy.

The priest stood at the altar, shaking a wand of paper streamers at us three times (purifying ceremony), then read the nuptials from a large manifold. Did Tomo understand a word of it? Ohana showed no trace of emotion, not once lifting her eyes. Each phase of the ceremony was signaled by a gong. There was no exchange of rings. Instead, the couple stood with heads bowed, drinking *sake* out of three different-sized golden goblets handed them by a pair of temple maidens in white linen blouses and red skirts. Then everybody sipped a little wine. To refuse meant that you disapproved of the marriage.

Everyone looked shocked when Tomo kissed Ohana. Following the rush of felicitating the bride and congratulating the groom, he threw his arms around me with a jubilant, "I'm the happiest man alive, Pete!"

I grinned. "That was fast work, Tomo."

"Well, I *had* to make time. You know we got on like a house afire from that first day. I proposed to her at Kamakura. Something happened inside me when I saw that Daibutsu — a kind of peace came over me, looking at the calm face. Sounds slushy, but — " He shook a cigarette from his pack. "We had this Shinto job to please Ohana's mother. Now we've got to be married again — a civil ceremony. No time for a honeymoon. We're flying to Korea Sunday, the twenty-fifth — "

"The day before I leave!"

Ohana, after introducing me to the middle-aged couple — her adopted parents — pressed my hand and said softly, "Bless you for bringing us together, Peter-chan." Her eyes danced with joy.

"By the time I get out of the army, my mother-in-law will be well enough to come to California. We'll be living near my folks." Tomo shook his head in admiration. "Great woman, really noble. And you know something? She *likes* me."

I smiled. The photographer's arrival stepped up the general excitement. Apparently there was to be no reception, so I slipped Ohana my little gift.

"Oh, thank you, Peter-chan! You'll forgive me if I'm rude and don't open it now. I have something for you, too." She pulled out of her sleeve pocket a tiny red and white amulet. "It's a Shinto charm. There's a wooden prayer tablet inside, but you must never open it. Promise?"

I nodded. "I'll wear it always. Thank you, Ohana. Well, Tomo, take care of her."

"Don't worry. And remember you have a standing invitation to stay with us." He dug me in the ribs. "I don't want to lose my first American brother."

I started home walking on air, gratified at the way everything had turned out. Tomo's problem was solved, I'd had a wonderful summer and there had been no unpleasantness. Then suddenly — zingo!

How that air-mail letter escaped my notice I'll never know. The envelope, marked "Personal," scared me. It was from a Boston law firm — Larry's father. What on earth could he be writing me about?

Dear Peter

Although I realize you're pretty young for this sort of letter, I feel that you can perhaps help more than any older friend of mine here in Boston. As you know, Larry is studying law at Boston University, where he met a Fulbright student. I have never met a nicer girl than Harumi, but it was a shock to hear that Larry intends to marry her. I am deeply disturbed. Don't think I'm an old fogy. It's just that I can see nothing but unhappiness for both of them. I simply don't understand young people any more. Of course he pays no attention to anything I say.

Perhaps I'm prejudiced, but I feel that Larry will go

far as a lawyer, and it will be a grave handicap for him
to marry a Japanese girl. I would rather have him
choose a girl not of his own faith than one of another
race. Besides, there may be children, and I hardly look
forward to being the grandfather of children with
mixed blood. Mind you, I have nothing against Harumi
herself. She is pleasing, well-mannered and very decorative. I don't object to Larry's taking her out occasionally, but she doesn't belong in our world.

I feel that because of your trip to Japan and your
long friendship with Larry you can speak with authority and probably influence him. Can you help me?

Yours in distress . . .

P.S. This is all in the strictest confidence, of course.

I dropped the letter, staggered that any one should ask a
high school boy to mix into such a serious matter. What
could *I* do? I just didn't have the gall to butt into Larry's
life. Ask Dad for his advice? Or get him to talk to Larry?
Tell Larry's father that I couldn't interfere?

Then slowly it dawned on me that I *did* have a right to
influence my friends. Because of what the AFS had done
for me, this *was* my responsibility. I couldn't funk taking a
stand. A few weeks ago I'd have said no, don't marry a
Japanese girl. Never the twain shall meet! The children
would be branded halfbreeds and persecuted. Now I wasn't
so sure. Of course Larry and Harumi would have to realize
what lay ahead. What really mattered was love and understanding. If the girl was as fine a type as Ohana or
Yoshi . . .

"Hands across the sea," Larry's father was saying in effect, "but let's keep our distance!" In this shrinking world

of ours, the concept of white supremacy was outmoded. Sheer bunkum. To believe that we were better than people with yellow skin and slanting eyes was as ridiculous as to think that tall people couldn't get along with short ones.

"The human heart is color-blind," I had read somewhere. "Let's hope that someday soon the human spirit will also be color-blind."

I decided to give Larry's father my answer in person when I got back.

XIX

GEISHA GIRLS — AT LAST

On our last night in Japan, Rai's uncle arranged for the governor of a Tokyo ward to give us a farewell party. After a delicious buffet supper in the garden of his home, Mr. Watanabe took us to a geisha house in the Shimbashi district — a red-lacquer structure as beautiful inside as out. I could only think of a luxurious Hollywood set.

We left our shoes at the entrance, walked across a red plush carpet to a *tatami*-covered level, through an elaborately painted paper door into a large reception room, and there were greeted by a bevy of sloe-eyed geishas so luscious that Jim Hauhart and I automatically reached for our cameras. While they posed, giggling, we snapped away, praying that the pictures would come out well. Otherwise folks at home would never believe we had seen the real Japan.

We were so dazzled that we didn't realize our party had gone upstairs. Searching for them, we kept opening wrong doors (smiles, apologies, interminable bows), until finally

Orientation

Jim Hauhart and Peter Bell with Geishas

A Man Can't Keep Out of Hot Water

Shoe-Fly

a geisha came to our rescue, guiding us through a maze of passageways to a room on the third floor.

The house was as cool as if air-conditioned. Tokyo sweltered that Sunday evening. We walked out on a balcony. A waterfall cascaded from a sprinkler system on the roof down into the patio where a fountain gurgled and sent up silver sprays. Fabulous! It was all so romantic that Jim had to yank me out of a trance.

While we knelt on cushions at a row of low tables, several *hangyoku* (junior geishas) glided into the room, carrying trays of delicacies — squid, snails, rice cakes, *sake*, Japanese beer and orange pop. Their mincing, coquettish walk entranced me. Every step they took flipped open the bottom of the kimono, exposing trim ankles. Their hair was lacquered and their kimonos exquisite, but I missed the white-washed faces and the ornate headpieces.

Each of us had a geisha. She fanned her guest and made light conversation. Mine was called O-Sei, which means purity. Meanwhile, a *hangyoku* plied us with *sake*, served in tiny gold and red porcelain cups. Guzzling rice wine and feeling very daring, I reflected there was something to be said for the life of an Oriental potentate.

When we were all relaxed and happy, five *hangyoku* slid into the room carrying *samisen* and *koto*. They sank gracefully to the floor and began plucking away with ivory picks, singing to the jangling, melancholy music. Their voices were hoarse and harsh, a quality, I understand, that is deliberately cultivated. The vocal chords are broken to the required tone by practice while the girl stands exposed to icy winter blasts. Later we watched a slow, measured dance, very intricate. They moved with the dignity of peacocks, their two-tone fans flashing, and always returning at the end of the number to the same kneeling posture, hiding their faces in their sleeves.

I was so spellbound that I drank more *sake* than was good for me. I didn't know what might happen if I stuck around much longer. Besides, I wanted to spend my last night with the Okajimas. So at eight-thirty I made my excuses. When Rai's uncle assigned me a geisha escort, I didn't know whether to feel complimented or insulted. Her name, O-Yasu, meant comfort.

"Something to tell my grandchildren about," I thought, walking through the streets of Tokyo with the glamorous geisha. Her English was limited to "Okay" and "You rike," while my Japanese was hardly any better. But I did catch enough of her native language to piece together her story.

She was only six when her father, a farmer near Kofu, sold her to one of the geisha agents who scour the country looking for pretty young girls. As an apprentice in a geisha school, O-Yasu learned to sing, dance, play musical instruments and develop all the feminine charms for which geishas are celebrated.

Did she like the life? She shrugged. Of course "Makata" had unionized geisha girls — an improvement. On the whole it was a pleasant career, if brief. She was now twenty-five. In another five years she would be *passé*. Then what? Well, many famous ex-geishas managed exclusive bars, restaurants or *ochaya* in Tokyo. If she was lucky, she might be set up in business by some rich admirer or else get a job as hostess in a teahouse. And that failing? Then it would be prostitution. O-Yasu spoke lightly, but behind her smile I sensed her tragic life.

When we reached the railroad station, she bowed, smiled and vanished.

Mrs. Okajima was amused at hearing about my first geisha experience. Kozo listened impassively, sitting under the *ka-kemono* in the Formal Room, his arms folded across his blue *yukata*. I asked the usual question: "Are geishas prostitutes?"

He shook his head vigorously. "*Yie, yie.*" Then, translating for his mother, he said they were highly cultivated entertainers, performing an important function, some of them confidantes of high-ranking officials. No stag party was complete without them. They broke the ice, cajoling, flattering, drawing out the guests. They were in great demand by businessmen entertaining out-of-town customers or Europeans. A man's social position was gauged by the number and quality of geishas he provided. Yes, they came high, the cost depending on the caliber of geisha engaged.

"Do they ever marry? Seldom. They were socially unacceptable. I was struck by the irony of it all. These beautiful creatures, whom Lafcadio Hearn called "the personification of joy," supplied all the feminine frills usually lacking in the average wife, whose place was of course at home.

It occurred to me that the system had its advantages. It took the burden of entertaining off Mama-san's shoulders. On the other hand, how unfair to be deprived of the pleasures her husband enjoyed! Why not geisha boys for lonely, bored housewives?

When I put that question to my foster mother, she looked

shocked and shifted the emphasis slightly, telling me about the geisha girl who had inspired Puccini to write his opera, *Madame Butterfly*. The wife of Thomas Glover, a wealthy British merchant, she lived with him and their son in a huge mansion overlooking the harbor at Nagasaki (Mrs. Okajima's birthplace). Mrs. Glover, a brilliant hostess, always wore kimonos splashed with butterflies, so her husband's foreign friends called her Madame Butterfly.

"No one know rest of real story," my foster mother concluded. "But maybe Madame Butterfry heart broken, rike radie in opera."

In her crimson kimono with the striped silver and blue *obi*, she looked like a butterfly herself. When I complimented her on the sash, she instantly called Haru-san and together they began opening treasure chests all over the house, spreading on *tatami* the four-yard lengths of gold, maroon, yellow, blue, green, lavender fabrics. A fantastic array worth a small fortune, I'm sure!

We spent the rest of the evening in the den, where she played the *samisen*, at my urging, and sang ancient folk melodies. Her voice faltered several times, and I got a lump in my throat whenever I thought of tomorrow. I said I wished I could stay until the end of October, having heard that autumn in Japan was indescribably beautiful.

"*So desu.*" She nodded, then sighed. "Happy time in life so short. But I hope you tell your Americans how you enjoy Japan and how it is in truth. Help my country and your country be friends, *ne?*"

"Of course." We sat reviewing my summer, talking until one A.M.

XX
SAYONARA

"Peetah-san, Peetah-san!" The maid pointed out the window in great excitement. "At last Honorable Fuji-san smile for you," she twittered in Japanese, so keyed up that she forgot to genuflect and kiss the floor that morning.

I crawled out of my *kaya* and stood beside her, rubbing my eyes. "Holy smoke!" After waiting nearly two months, what a thrill to get my first and only glimpse of Fuji! There it was in all its grandeur, as symmetrical as an inverted fan, the snowy crest shell-pink in the morning light. Like a farewell gift. I dashed downstairs to tell the Okajimas. They were delighted and said it was a good omen.

For my last breakfast Mrs. Okajima had prepared my favorite dishes — bird's-nest (thinly shaved potato curls arranged around two poached eggs) and "squirrels' eggs." Yoshi had explained that they were actually tiny birds.

All that morning we tried to behave like "splendid Japanese," pinning on smiles. But Mrs. Okajima kept murmuring sadly, "Last *asa-gohan*, last *futon*, last *tatami!*" The beautiful geisha doll she gave me would be forwarded in a Philippine mahogany box, but where could I stow the hand-carved tray? I had arrived with three pieces of luggage. Now I had six, and every one stuffed to the top. Would I ever survive on the SS *Cleveland?* Then suddenly Mrs. Okajima gave an agonized cry. We had overlooked one drawer in the *tansu.* Haru-san hastily stuffed shirts, sweaters and underwear into the already crammed overnight bag, much to her mistress's anguish.

Kozo and I rushed out, riding tandem on his bike and snapping last-minute pictures. I stopped to buy a pair of *geta,* as I intended giving illustrated talks in Gloucester schools and clubs clad in full Japanese regalia. I had taken six hundred snapshots (thirty rolls) and planned to wind up those talks with a shot of Nikko's red-lacquer bridge — the bridge of friendship!

Back at the house, we ate a chicken lunch, the atmosphere as gloomy as a graveyard. Kozo and his mother were to see me off at Yokohama. I dreaded saying good-by to Haru-san. How could I thank her for her everlasting kindness? She had presented me with a handmade *yukata,* and I didn't dare give her a thing. A farewell present, I was told, would be inappropriate. The sea-gull brooch I had bought her would go to Yoshi, whose birthday fell on the same day as mine — August 31. It was a change of mind, not of heart. I just hoped that photograph of Haru-san would turn out okay.

"*Sayonara,* Peetah-san!" Standing in the doorway in her red-checked gingham and white kerchief, she wore the same sweet smile which had greeted me two months ago.

I mumbled my thanks and bowed, strongly tempted to hug her. *"Sayonara!"* The saddest word in any language. "Wish somebody would find her a nice husband," I said, waving to her from the car.

"I find her one." Mrs. Okajima smiled understandingly, arranging the striped *obi* of her white polka-dot kimono.

We had been driving about fifteen minutes, joking nervously about missing the boat, when suddenly I thought of my ticket. I searched my pockets. It wasn't there. My face was on fire. Nothing to do but go back. Anticlimax!

"Itte mairimasu!" (I go only to return) I rushed past a surprised Haru-san — she must have thought me crazy — grabbed the ticket in my room, flew downstairs muttering, "Page Freud," then planted a loud kiss on her cheek. She almost fainted as I bolted through the door, shouting, *"Sayonara!"* Now I knew why I had left that ticket behind.

The SS *Cleveland* was to sail at four P.M. We made Yokohama in plenty of time for me to go through immigration, customs and quarantine. Little Hiroko and her beautiful mother, both in matching kimonos, had joined us. In all the din and hubbub Rai was buttonholing us and trying to get our signatures to one hundred and fifty bread-and-butter letters. He said that two hundred and fifty international students were en route to American and Canadian universities. More links in the chain of good-will envoys!

At three P.M. the whistle blew and there was a mad scramble of passengers and visitors aboard. When I saw Dr. Norman Vincent Peale and his family walking up the gangplank, I realized I was really going home. As Kozo helped carry my bags to the hold (this time I had a lower

berth), I wondered if he would find his soul mate in Koharu. On deck once more, I stumbled into the lounge to say
good-by to the AFS committee members in Japan. That
was a tough assignment.

"See you at the U.N. in 1962, when we both graduate."
Rai gave me the usual blacksmith's grip.

Parting from Yoshi was painful. This modest girl and devoted AFSer had been dear to our hearts. She broke down
when I gave her the birthday brooch. "I'll see you someday
for sure!" My bravado covered an ache and emptiness.

Altogether it was a damp, humid party. Kate Lowry hid
her red eyes behind a tiny Japanese flag, Pete Martin kept
dabbing at his eyes, Arthur's handkerchief grew wetter and
wetter despite his jokes and attempts at clowning, while
Dave concealed his emotion behind those dark goggles. He
had left his large and affectionate foster family in tears at
the Fukui railway station, with solemn pledges to meet
again soon. A photographer from *Life* magazine had shot
pictures of him for four days, "wasting fifty rolls of film
on me."

The buzzers sounded. Over the P.A. system came the
purser's, "All visitors ashore, please!" Among the push and
pull of the outgoing throng, I kissed little Hiroko, shook
hands with her mother, then braced myself to say good-by
to Mrs. Okajima.

"Prease excuse — I want say you this," she began unstead-
ily. "You are rike my son — rike another Kozo. When door
of heart open wide, is no more race, is no more nation, is
just one beeg famiry." There was a catch in her voice. "We
write often each other, *ne?*"

I was too deeply moved to speak. When she violated two rules, kissing me and crying, Kozo looked embarrassed and shocked. His handshake was firmer than his voice as he said, "See you rater, arrigator!" We clapped each other on the shoulder and that was it.

Our coeds wept openly as the liner pulled out. Two months ago a handful of people had welcomed us. Now there was a large crowd — friends old and new from all over Japan, shouting, "*Banzai*" and "*Sayonara*." We caught the colored streamers they flung from the dock and I grabbed hold of Kozo's, exchanging a final "*Sayonara*."

During dinner, the ship's band played "The Brave One." I felt anything but brave. My head whirled like a kaleidoscope with thoughts and memories — the Gold Pavilion in Kyoto, the cripples and beggars at the temples, Tomo's wistful, "I don't belong anywhere," ragged urchins looking up at the rain and saying, "Strontium 90," Larry's father with his "hands across the sea but keep your distance," Mrs. Okajima's motto, "To make the world more wonderful" —

Yes, I had an *on*, a lifelong *on* — to Japan. So did America — to all the races that had made her strong, rich and powerful. Our *on* was world-wide and eternal. Of all peoples on earth we had the least right to arrogance or intolerance. Most of our fears about strange peoples are like Kouno's artificial snake. There are no fangs. As my foster mother had said, "When door of heart open wide, is no more race, is no more nation, is just one beeg famiry."

Say onara

GLOSSARY

ame — a sticky sweet; wheat gluten
ano-ne — it's like this
arigato — thank you
atsui-ne — hot, isn't it?
baka — damned fool
banzai — a thousand years of good luck
benjo — toilet
beru — bell
biru — beer
bonsai — dwarfed trees, full-grown
butsudan — altar built in the wall
casa — umbrella
chan — affectionate diminutive suffix
cohi-shopu — coffee shop

dai — great; big
daijōbu — all right
daimyo — war lords
dame — bad; spoiled; improper
domo arigato gozaimasu — thank you very much
dozo — please
enu — dogs
furoshiki — large bandanna for shopping and travel
futon — thin mattress
garu — girl
geisha — accomplished entertainer
geta — wooden shoes
gohan — cooked rice
gomen kudasai — pardon me
gomen nasai — excuse me

hai — yes
haikai — poem
haikei — crippled soldier
hanabi — fireworks
hana-michi — flower bridge
hangyoku — young geisha girls
hara-kiri — suicide by stabbing
haro — hello
hashi — chopsticks
hibachi — charcoal burner
ichi ban — number one
irasshai — welcome
homu-runu — home run
jan-ken-po — the paper-scissors-stone game
jin — human being; person
jochu — female servant
junsa — police
kabuki — traditional drama, all-male cast
kakemono — picture scroll
kami — god
kamikaze — suicide (literally, god-wind)
kaya — mosquito tent
kekko — splendid
kiku — chrysanthemum
koibito — sweetheart

komuso — temple priests
konban-wa — good evening
koto — harplike instrument
ku — ward or district
Lumpen (German) — beggar
matsuri — festival
mompei — overalls
mon — family crest
moshi — hello
nakōdo — matchmaker
neesan — servant; also, older sister
Nisei — American-born Japanese
Noh — highly symbolic drama; actors masked
Obā-san — grandmother
O-bento — box lunches
obi — sash
ocha — tea
ochaya — teahouse
ohayo gozaimasu — good morning
oi, oi — hey, hey
oishi — delicious
O-furo — bath
Okā-san — mother
O-kashi — soybean cakes
on — debt

ooki — big
orenji juisu — orange juice
O-shibori — damp face cloths
Otō-san — father
oyasumi nasai — good night
pachinko — pinball machine
pan — bread
sake — rice wine
samisen — banjolike instrument
sampan — fishing boat
san — Miss, Mister or Mrs.
sanpatsu-ya — barbershop
sayonara — good-by
sembei — rice cakes
sensei — teacher; master
shikata ga nai — it can't be helped
shinju — pearl
shogun — feudal ruler
shujin — husband
shukan — custom
so desu — it is
so desu-ka — is that right?
sukiyaki — beef and vegetable dish
sumimasen — I'm sorry
sumo — wrestling; wrestler
suteki — glorious

Sutro — Buddhist prayer
tabi — white mittenlike socks
tabun — maybe
tachiaoi — blossoming bush
takusan — very much
tanabata — seventh day of the seventh month
tansu — chest of drawers
tatami — floor matting
tempura — fried sea food or vegetables
tera — Buddhist temple
tofu — bean curd
tokonoma — alcove of honor
torii — open Shinto shrine gate
tsuyu — rainy season
yadoya — inn
yagura — a high stage; turret
yaki-mori — seaweed
yen — 1/350 of a dollar
yie — no
yofuko — Western garb
yoi yoisho — yo-heave-ho
yūjō — friendship
yukata — unlined cotton kimono
zabutan — pillow
zōri — straw sandals